Dinah Zike's

Big Book of
Math

Grade Levels K-6

Dinah Zike, M.Ed.

Office (210) 698-0123
Fax (210) 698-0095
Orders only: 1-800-99DINAH (993-4624)
Orders or catalog requests: orders@dinah.com
E-mail: dma@dinah.com
Website: www.dinah.com
ISBN Number: 1-882796-22-5

HPS218668

Table of Contents

Dear Teacher:

What is a Foldable?

A Foldable is a 3-D, student-made, interactive graphic organizer based upon a skill. Making a Foldable gives students a fast, kinesthetic activity that helps them organize and retain information. Foldables are designed to be used as a study guide for main ideas and key points; however, Foldables can also be used to solve math problems, answer questions, explain computations, and record definitions. The purpose of this book is to give you countless ways in which you can individualize Foldables to meet your curriculum needs.

Who, What, When, Why?

You probably have seen at least one of the Foldables featured in this book used in supplemental programs or staff-development workshops. Today, my Foldables are used internationally. I present workshops and keynotes to over fifty thousand teachers and parents a year, sharing Foldables that I began inventing, designing, and adapting over thirty-five years ago. Students of all ages are using them for daily work, note-taking activities, student-directed projects, forms of alternative assessment, journals, graphs, tables, and more.

Add and Amend

After workshop presentations, participants would ask me for lists of activities to be used with the Foldables they had just learned to make. They needed help visualizing how to convert math data into Foldables. So, over fifteen years ago, I began collecting and sharing the ideas listed in this book. The ideas are organized by topic. The table for each topic shows the math content being addressed and an appropriate Foldable.

I now hand these lists of ideas and information over to you and your students. Have fun using, adding to, and amending them.

Workshops
1-210-698-0123
jeanne@dinah.com

Orders
1-800-99DINAH
orders@dinah.com
www.dinah.com

E-Group
Join on website:
www.dinah.com

Why use Foldables in Math?

When teachers ask me why they should take time to use the Foldables featured in this book, I explain that they

. . . quickly organize, display, and arrange data, making it easier for students to grasp math concepts and master skills.

. . . result in student-made study guides that are compiled as students listen for main ideas, read for main ideas, and work their way through new concepts and procedures.

. . . provide a multitude of creative formats in which students can present projects, research, interviews, and inquiry-based reports instead of typical poster board or math fair formats.

. . . replace teacher-generated writing or photocopied sheets with student-generated print.

. . . incorporate the use of such skills as comparing and contrasting, recognizing cause and effect, and finding similarities and differences into daily work and long-term projects. For example, these Foldables can be used to compare and contrast student explanations and procedures for solving problems to the explanations presented by other students and teachers.

. . . continue to "immerse" students in previously learned vocabulary, and concepts, providing them with a strong foundation that they can build upon with new observations, experiences, and knowledge.

. . . can be used by students or teachers to easily communicate data through graphs, tables, charts, models, and diagrams, including Venn diagrams.

. . . allow students to make their own math journals for recording main ideas, problem-solving strategies, examples, questions that arise during classwork, and personal experiences that occur during learning.

. . . can be used as alternative assessment tools by teachers to evaluate student progress or by students to evaluate their own progress.

. . . integrate language arts, the sciences, and social studies into the study of mathematics.

. . . provide a sense of student ownership or investment in the mathematics curriculum.

National Math Standards and Communication Skills

The Principles and Standards for School Mathematics, published by the National Council of Teachers of Mathematics (NCTM) in 2000, stress the importance of communication skills in a strong mathematics program. Not all students will become mathematicians, engineers, or statisticians, but all students need to be able to think, analyze, and problem solve using skills acquired through the study of mathematics.

Throughout their lives, students will be called upon to be literate in mathematics—personally and professionally. They will need to have a basic understanding of numbers, operations, and quantitative reasoning; patterns, relationships, and algebraic thinking; geometry; measurement; and probability and statistics to solve real-life problems involving finances, chance, design, science, fine arts, and more.

Furthermore, students must be able to share the results of their use of mathematics using various forms of oral and written communication. Foldables are one of many techniques that can be used to integrate reading, writing, thinking, organizing data, researching, and other communication skills into an interdisciplinary mathematics curriculum.

Foldable Basics

What to Write and Where

Teach students to write general information--titles, vocabulary words, concepts, questions, main ideas, and laws or theorems--on the front tabs of their Foldables. General information is viewed every time a student looks at a Foldable. Foldables help students focus on and remember key points without being distracted by other print.

Ask students to write specific information—supporting ideas, student thoughts, answers to questions, research information, empirical data, class notes, observations, and definitions—under the tabs.

As you teach, demonstrate different ways in which Foldables can be used. Soon you will find that students make their own Foldables and use them independently for study guides and projects.

With or Without Tabs

Foldables with flaps or tabs create study guides that students can use to self check what they know about the general information on the front of tabs. Use Foldables without tabs for assessment purposes (where it's too late to self check) or projects where information is presented for others to view quickly.

Venn Diagram used as a study guide

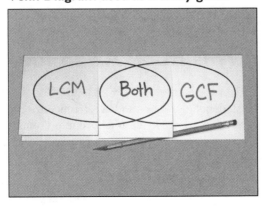

Venn Diagram used for assessment

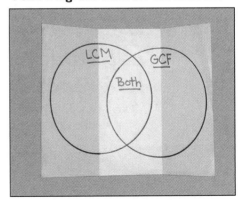

What to Do with Scissors and Glue

If it is difficult for your students to keep glue and scissors at their desks or to carry it from class to class, set up a small table in the classroom and provide several containers of glue, numerous pairs of scissors (sometimes tied to the table), containers of crayons or colored pencils, a stapler, clear tape, and anything else you think students might need to make their Foldables. Don't be surprised if students donate colored markers, decorative-edged scissors, gel pens, stencils, and other art items to your publishing table.

The more they make and use graphic organizers, the faster students become at producing them.

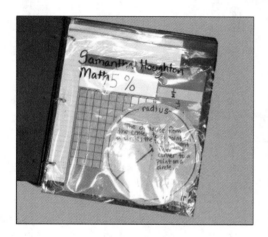

Storing Graphic Organizers in Student Portfolios

Turn one-gallon freezer bags into student portfolios which can be collected and stored in the classroom. Students can also carry their portfolios in their notebooks if they place strips of two-inch clear tape along one side and punch three holes through the taped edge.

Have each student write his or her name along the top of the plastic portfolio with a permanent marker and cover the writing with two-inch clear tape to keep it from wearing off.

Cut the bottom corners off the bag so it won't hold air and will stack and store easily.

HINT: *I found it more convenient to keep student portfolios in my classroom so student work was always available when needed and not "left at home" or "in the car." Giant laundry-soap boxes make good storage containers for portfolios.*

Let Students Use This Book As an Idea Reference

Make this book of lists available to students to use as an idea reference for projects, discussions, social studies debates, extra credit work, cooperative learning group presentations, and more.

Selecting the Appropriate Foldable

Dividing Math Concepts into Parts

Foldables divide information and make it visual. In order to select the appropriate Foldable, decide how many parts you want to divide the information into and then determine which Foldable best illustrates or fits those parts. Foldables that are three-dimensional also make the student interact with the data kinesthetically.

For example, if you are studying the Fundamental Laws of Algebra you could choose a Foldable that has five tabs (or sections), on the front tabs write the laws, and under the tabs, explain the laws in words on one side, and in symbols on the other side.

Math Concepts Already Divided into Parts					
Whole Numbers		**Geometry**		**Measurement**	
Parts	Concept	Parts	Concept	Parts	Concept
4	addition, subtraction, multiplication, division	2	complimentary and supplementary angles	3	length, width, heigth
2	inequalities, $<$ and $>$	2	convex and concave	5	pennies, nickels, dimes, quarters, half dollars
3	equalities and inequalities, $<, =, >$	3	translation, rotation, reflection	2	kilometers and meters
2	inverse operations	6	types of triangles	4	gallons, half gallons, quarts, pints
2	properties of addition and multiplication	2	types of right triangles	2	ounces and pounds
2	prime and composite numbers	6	types of quadrilaterals	3	hours, minutes, seconds
2	ordinal and cardinal numbers	2	x-axis and y-axis	4	day, week, month, year

Math Concepts That Can Be Divided into Parts		
Whole Numbers	**Geometry**	**Statistics and Probability**
number lines	draw angles with a protractor	determine ranges of sets
sets	classify polygons	interpret scatter plots
arrays	illustrate quadrilaterals	display data collected in plots
place value	list examples of prisms	draw models of combinations
word problems	name ordered pairs	
properties	graph points	

Dividing Skills and Foldables into Parts

Reading, writing, and thinking skills can easily be used with Foldables. The following lists show examples of skills and activities and a selection of Foldables divided into parts. You may want to refer to this page as you select activities from the lists of math topics in the third section of this book (see pages 44–88).

Skills and Activities Divided into Parts	
1 Part	**2 Parts**
Find the Main Idea	Compare and Contrast
Predict an Outcome	Cause and Effect
Narrative Writing	Similarities and Differences
Descriptive Writing	Opposite Operations
Expository Writing	
Persuasive Writing	
3 Parts	**4 Parts**
Venn Diagrams	Who, What, When, Where
Know?-Like to Know?-Learned?	What, Where, When, Why/How
Beginning, Middle, End	Four Operations
Any Number of Parts	
Questioning	Making and Using Tables
Flow Charts	Making and Using Graphs
Vocabulary Words	Making and Using Charts
Time Lines	Sequencing Data or Events
Concept Webs or Maps	

Foldables Divided into Parts	
1 Part	**2 Parts**
Half Book	Two-Tab Book
Folded Book	Pocket Book
Three-Quarter Book	Shutterfold
Picture-Frame Book	Matchbook Cut in Half
Bound Book	Forward-Backward Book
Matchbook	Concept Map with Two Tabs
3 Parts	**4 Parts**
Trifold Book	Four-Tab Book
Three-Tab Book	Standing Cube
Pyramid Book	Top-Tab Book
Three Pocket Book	Four-Door Book
Concept Map with Three Tabs	
Any Number of Parts	
Accordion Book	Circle Graph
Layered-Look Book	Concept-Map Book
Sentence-Strip Holder	Vocabulary Book
Sentence Strips	Pyramid Mobile
Bound Book	Pop-Up Book
Top-Tab Book (three or more sheets of paper)	Multiple-Pocket Books
Billboard Project	Project Board with Tabs
Display Case	Folded Table, Chart, or Graph

Basic Foldable Shapes

The following figures illustrate the basic folds that are referred to throughout the following section of this book

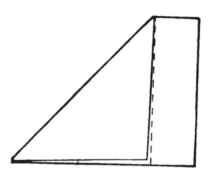

Taco Fold

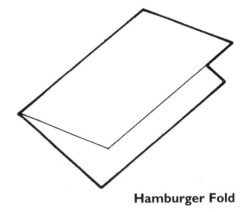

Hamburger Fold

Hot Dog Fold

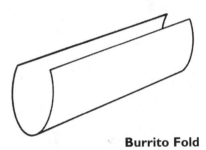

Burrito Fold

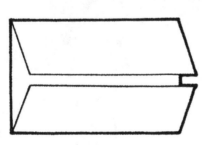

Shutter Fold

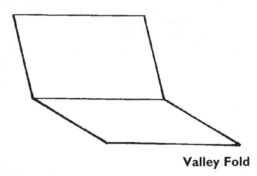

Valley Fold

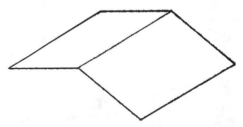

Mountain Fold

Half-Book

Fold a sheet of paper (8 1/2" χ 11") in half.

1. This book can be folded vertically like a *hot dog* or . . .

2. . . . it can be folded horizontally like a *hamburger.*

Use this book for descriptive, expository, persuasive, or narrative writing, as well as graphs, diagrams, or charts.

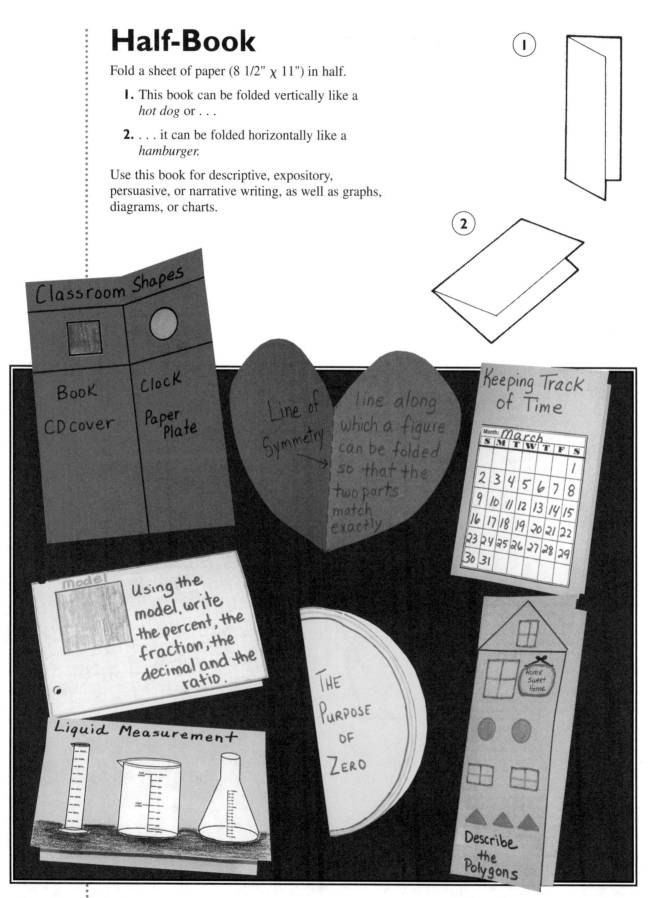

Folded Book

1. Make a *half-book.*

2. Fold it in half again like a *hamburger.* This makes a ready-made cover, and two small pages for information on the inside.

Use photocopied work sheets, Internet print outs, and student-drawn diagrams or graphs to make this book. One sheet of paper becomes two activities and two grades.

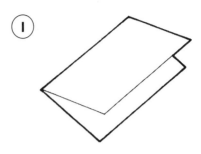

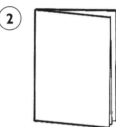

Step 1

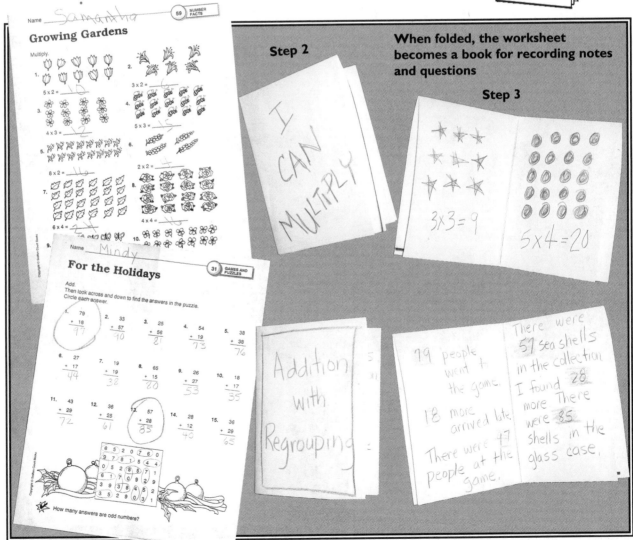

Step 2

When folded, the worksheet becomes a book for recording notes and questions

Step 3

Three-Quarter Book

1. Take a *two-tab* book and raise the left-hand tab.

2. Cut the tab off at the top fold line.

3. A larger book of information can be made by gluing several *three-quarter books* side-by-side.

Sketch or glue a graphic to the left, write one or more questions on the right, and record answers and information under the right tab.

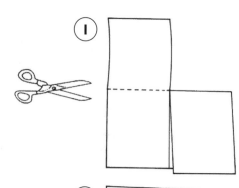

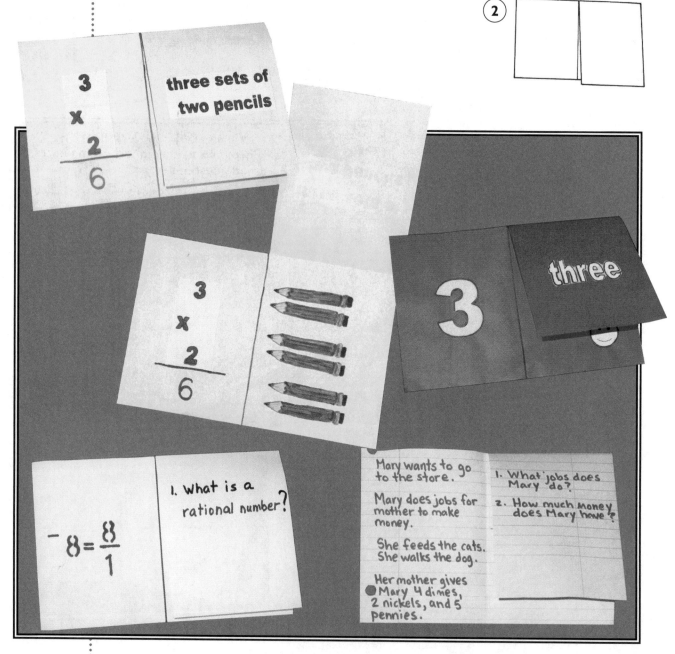

Bound Book

1. Take two sheets of paper (8 1/2" χ 11") and separately fold them like a *hamburger.* Place the papers on top of each other, leaving one sixteenth of an inch between the *mountain tops.*

2. Mark both folds one inch from the outer edges.

3. On one of the folded sheets, cut from the top and bottom edge to the marked spot on both sides.

4. On the second folded sheet, start at one of the marked spots and cut the fold between the two marks.

5. Take the cut sheet from step 3 and fold it like a *burrito.* Place the *burrito* through the other sheet and then open the *burrito.* Fold the bound pages in half to form an eight-page book.

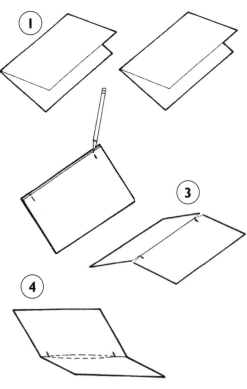

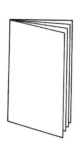

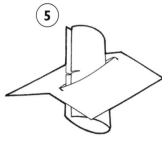

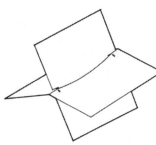

Picture-Frame Book

I. Fold a sheet of paper (8 1/2" χ 11") in half like a *hamburger*.

2. Open the *hamburger* and gently roll one side of the *hamburger* toward the *valley*. Try not to crease the roll.

3. Cut a rectangle out of the middle of the rolled side of the paper leaving a half-inch border, forming a frame.

4. Fold another sheet of paper (8 1/2" χ 11") in half like a *hamburger.* Apply glue to the inside border of the picture frame and place the folded, uncut sheet of paper inside.

Use this book to feature a person, place, or thing. Inside the picture frames, glue photographs, magazine pictures, computer-generated graphs, or have students sketch pictures. This book has three inside pages for writing and recording notes.

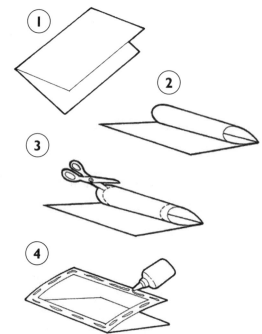

Two-Tab Book

1. Take a *folded book* and cut up the *valley* of the inside fold toward the *mountain top*. This cut forms two large tabs that can be used front and back for writing and illustrations.

2. The book can be expanded by making several of these folds and gluing them side-by-side.

Use this book with data occurring in twos. For example, use it for comparing and contrasting, determining cause and effect, finding similarities and differences, and more.

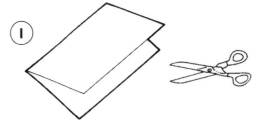

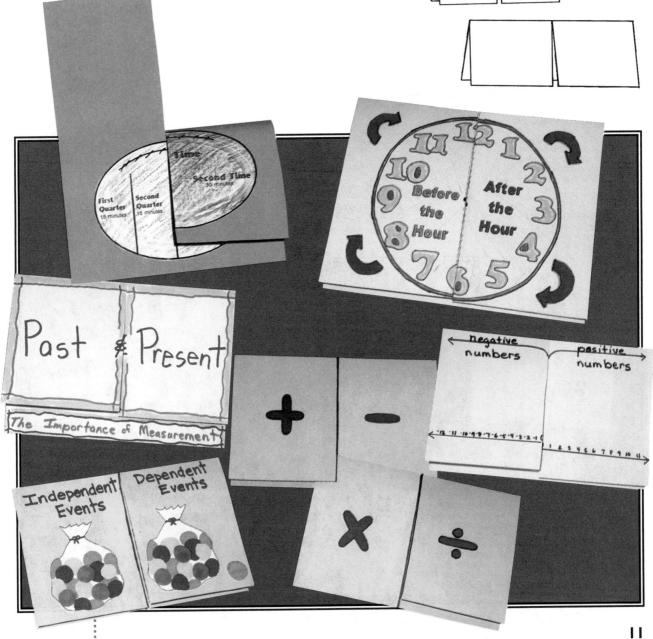

Pocket Book

1. Fold a sheet of paper (8 1/2" χ 11") in half like a *hamburger.*

2. Open the folded paper and fold one of the long sides up two inches to form a pocket. Refold along the *hamburger* fold so that the newly formed pockets are on the inside.

3. Glue the outer edges of the two-inch fold with a small amount of glue.

4. Optional:• Glue a cover around the *pocket book.*

Variation: Make a multi-paged booklet by gluing several pockets side-by-side. Glue a cover around the multi-paged *pocket book.*

Use 3" χ 5" index cards and quarter-sheets of notebook paper inside the pockets. Store student-made books, such as two-tab books and folded books in the pockets.

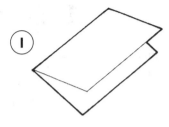

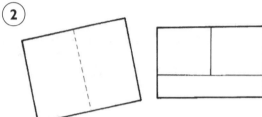

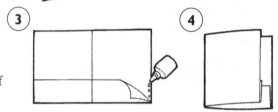

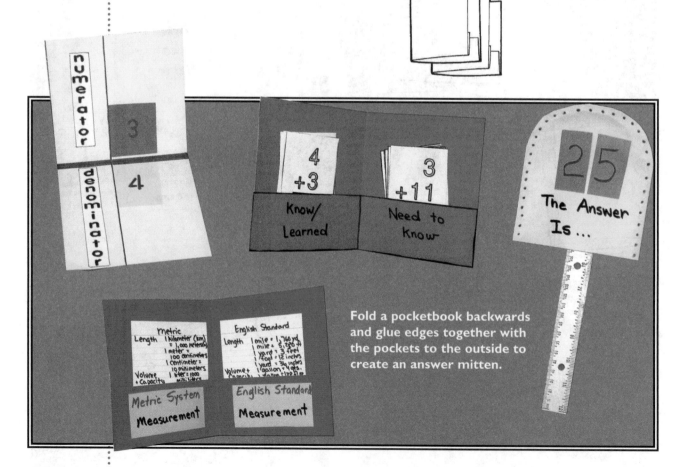

Fold a pocketbook backwards and glue edges together with the pockets to the outside to create an answer mitten.

Matchbook

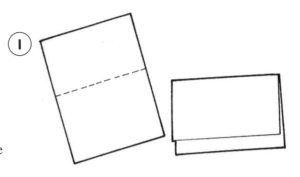

1. Fold a sheet of paper (8 1/2" χ 11") like a *hamburger,* but fold it so that one side is one inch longer than the other side.

2. Fold the one-inch tab over the short side forming an envelopelike fold.

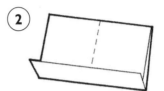

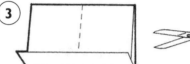

3. Cut the front flap in half toward the *mountain top* to create two flaps.

Collect matchbooks and use them to make classroom bulletin boards.

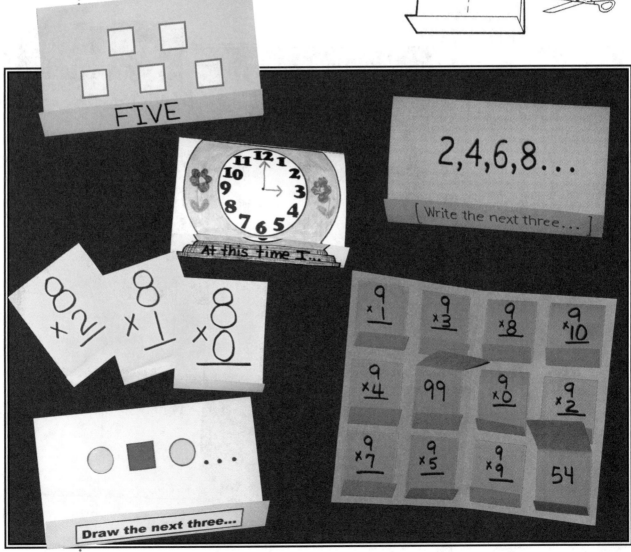

Shutter Fold

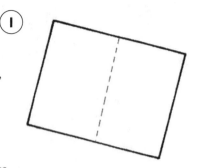

1. Begin as if you were going to make a *hamburger* but instead of creasing the paper, pinch it to show the midpoint.

2. Fold the outer edges of the paper to meet at the pinch, or mid-point, forming a *shutter fold.*

Use this book for data occurring in twos. Or, make this fold using 11" χ 17" paper and smaller books—such as the half book, journal, and two-tab book—that can be glued inside to create a large project full of student work.

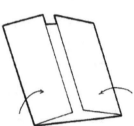

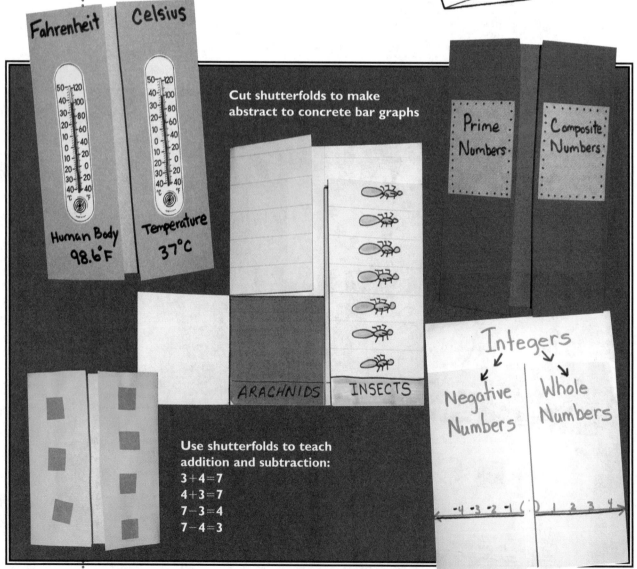

Cut shutterfolds to make abstract to concrete bar graphs

Fahrenheit

Celsius

Human Body 98.6°F

Temperature 37°C

Prime Numbers

Composite Numbers

ARACHNIDS

INSECTS

Integers

Negative Numbers

Whole Numbers

-4 -3 -2 -1 0 1 2 3 4

Use shutterfolds to teach addition and subtraction:

3+4=7
4+3=7
7−3=4
7−4=3

Forward-Backward Book

1. Stack three or more sheets of paper. On the top sheet trace a large circle.

2. With the papers still stacked, cut out the circles.

3. Staple the paper circles together along the left-hand side to create a book.

4. Label the cover and takes notes on the pages that open to the right.

5. Turn the book upside down and label the back. Takes notes on the pages that open to the right.

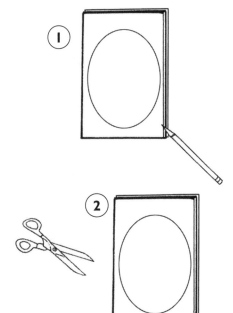

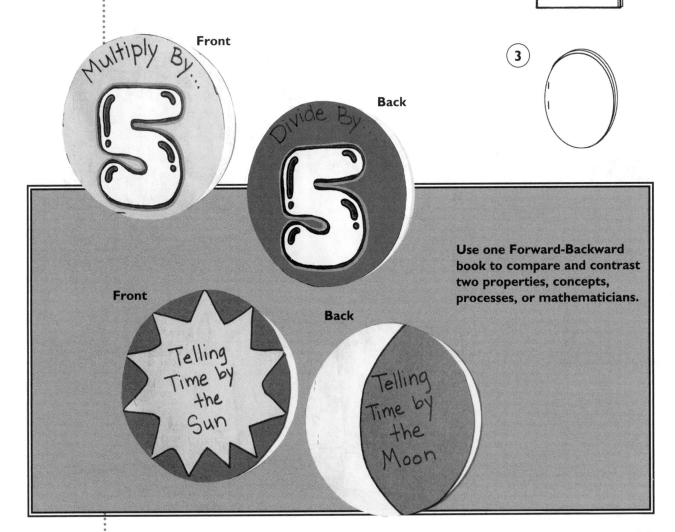

Use one Forward-Backward book to compare and contrast two properties, concepts, processes, or mathematicians.

Three-Tab Book

1. Fold a sheet of paper like a *hot dog*.

2. With the paper horizontal, and the fold of the *hot dog* up, fold the right side toward the center, trying to cover one half of the paper.

NOTE: *If you fold the right edge over first, the final graphic organizer will open and close like a book.*

3. Fold the left side over the right side to make a book with three folds.

4. Open the folded book. Place your hands between the two thicknesses of paper and cut up the two *valleys* on one side only. This will form three tabs.

Use this book for data occurring in threes such as three properties: Associative, Distributive, And Commutative.

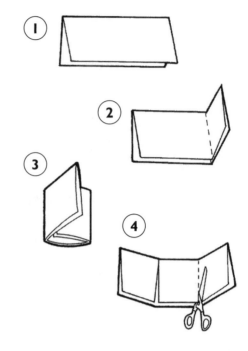

Three-Tab Book Variations

VARIATION A:
Draw overlapping circles on the three tabs to make a Venn Diagram

VARIATION B:
Cut each of the three tabs in half to make a six-tab book.

A.
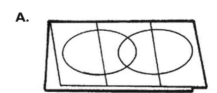

B.

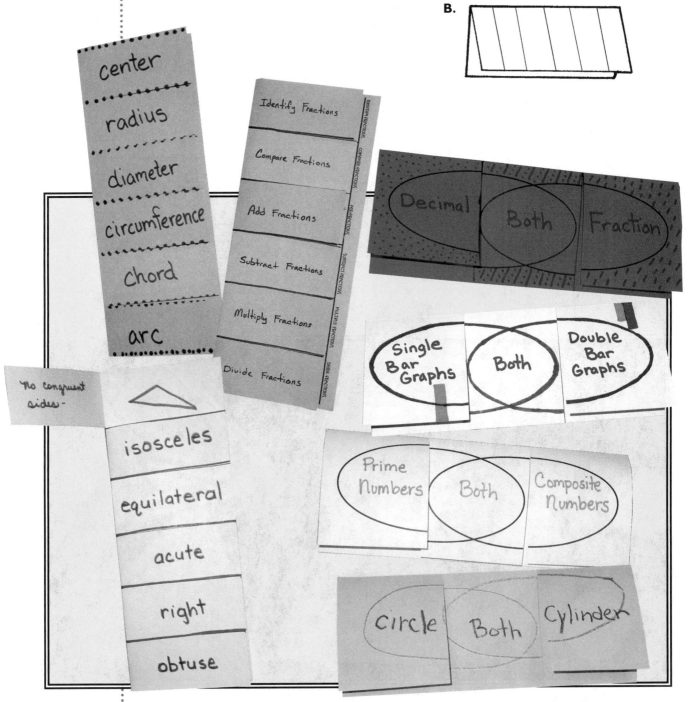

Pyramid Fold

1. Fold a sheet of paper (8 1/2" χ 11") into a *taco,* forming a square. Cut off the excess rectangular tab formed by the fold.

2. Open the folded *taco* and refold it the opposite way forming another *taco* and an X-fold pattern.

3. Cut one of the folds to the center of the X, or the midpoint, and stop. This forms two triangular-shaped flaps.

4. Glue one of the flaps under the other, forming a *pyramid.*

5. Label front sections and write information, notes, thoughts, and questions inside the pyramid on the back of the appropriate tab.

Use to make mobiles and dioramas.
Use with data occurring in threes.

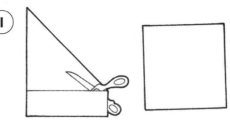

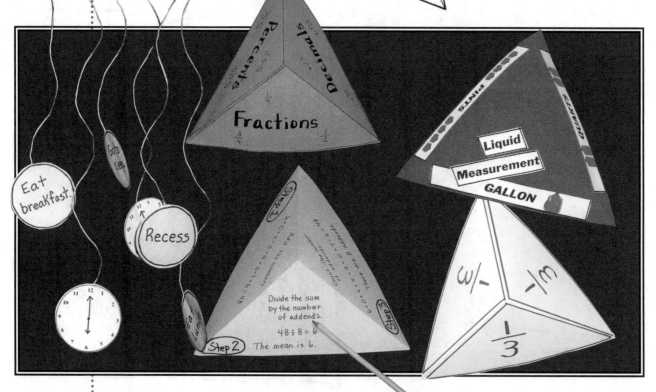

Trifold Book

1. Fold a sheet of paper (8 1/2" χ 11") into thirds.

2. Use this book as is, or cut into shapes. If the trifold is cut, leave plenty of fold on both sides of the designed shape, so the book will open and close in three sections.

Use this book to make charts with three columns or rows, large Venn diagrams, reports on data occurring in threes, or to show the outside and inside of something and to write about it.

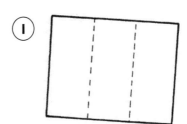

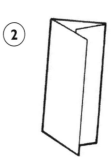

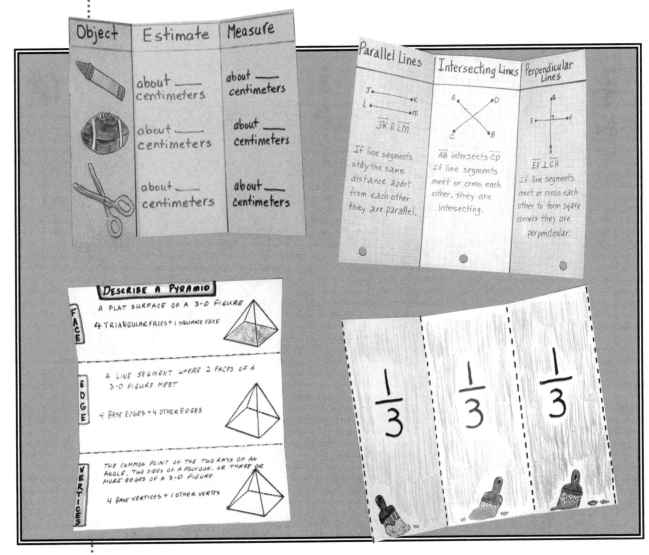

Three Pocket Book

1. Fold a horizontal sheet of paper (11" χ 17") into thirds.

2. Fold the bottom edge up two inches and crease well. Glue the outer edges of the two inch tab to create three pockets.

3. Label each pocket. Use to hold notes taken on index cards or quarter sheets of paper.

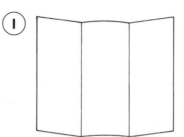

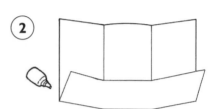

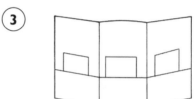

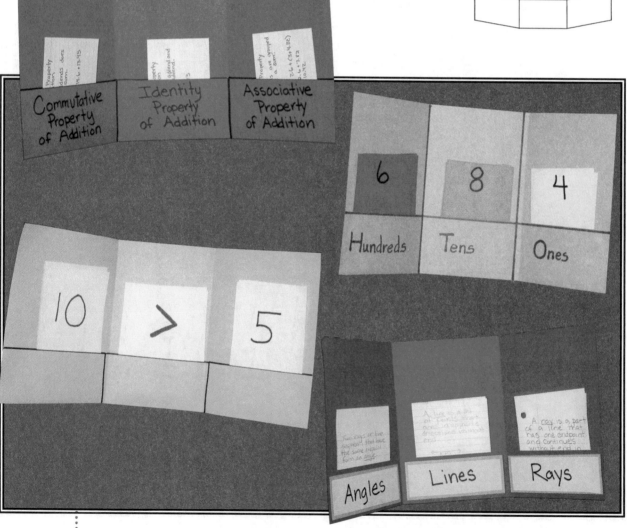

Four-Tab Book

1. Fold a sheet of paper (8 1/2" χ 11") in half like a *hot dog*.

2. Fold this long rectangle in half like a *hamburger*.

3. Fold both ends back to touch the *mountain top* or fold it like an *accordion*.

4. On the side with two *valleys* and one *mountain top*, make vertical cuts through one thickness of paper, forming four tabs.

Use this book for data occurring in fours. For example: addition, subtraction, multiplication, and division of integers.

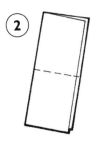

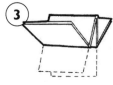

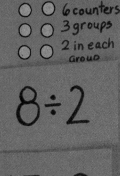

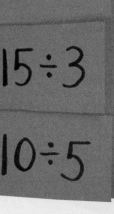

○ ○ 6 counters
○ ○ 3 groups
○ ○ 2 in each group

$8 \div 2$

$15 \div 3$

$10 \div 5$

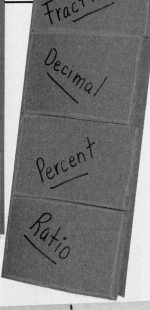

Fraction

Decimal

Percent

Ratio

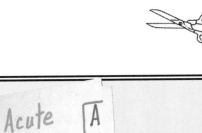

Acute

Right

Obtuse

Straight

A N G L E S

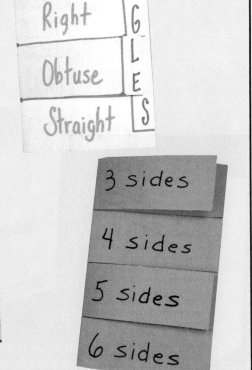

3 sides

4 sides

5 sides

6 sides

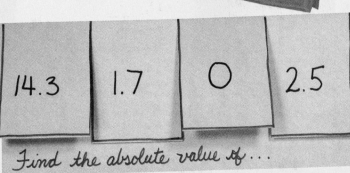

| 14.3 | 1.7 | 0 | 2.5 |

Find the absolute value of . . .

Standing Cube

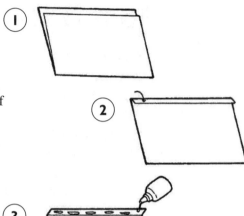

1. Use two sheets of the same size paper. Fold each like a *hamburger*. However, fold one side one half inch shorter than the other side. This will make a tab that extends out one half inch on one side.

2. Fold the long side over the short side of both sheets of paper, making tabs.

3. On one of the folded papers, place a small amount of glue along the the small folded tab, next to the *valley* but not in it.

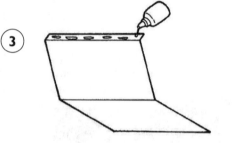

4. Place the non-folded edge of the second sheet of paper square into the *valley* and fold the glue-covered tab over this sheet of paper. Press flat until the glue holds. Repeat with the other side.

5. Allow the glue to dry completely before continuing. After the glue has dried, the cube can be collapsed flat to allow students to work at their desks. The cube can also be folded into fourths for easier storage, or for moving it to a display area.

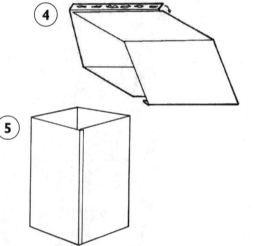

Use with data occurring in fours or make it into a project. Make a small display cube using 8 1/2" χ 11" paper. Use 11" χ 17" paper to make large project cubes that you can glue other books onto for display. Notebook paper, photocopied sheets, magazine pictures, and current events also can be displayed on the large cube.

This large cube project can be folded and stored in plastic bag portfolios.

Four-Door Book

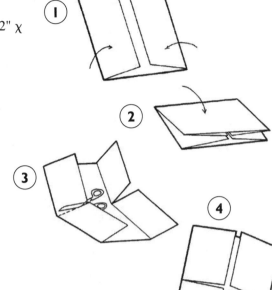

1. Make a *shutter fold* using 11" χ 17" or 12" χ 18" paper.

2. Fold the *shutter fold* in half like a *hamburger.* Crease well.

3. Open the project and cut along the two inside *valley* folds.

4. These cuts will form four doors on the inside of the project.

Use this fold for data occurring in fours. When folded in half like a *hamburger,* a finished *four-door book* can be glued inside a large (11" χ 17") *shutter fold* as part of a larger project.

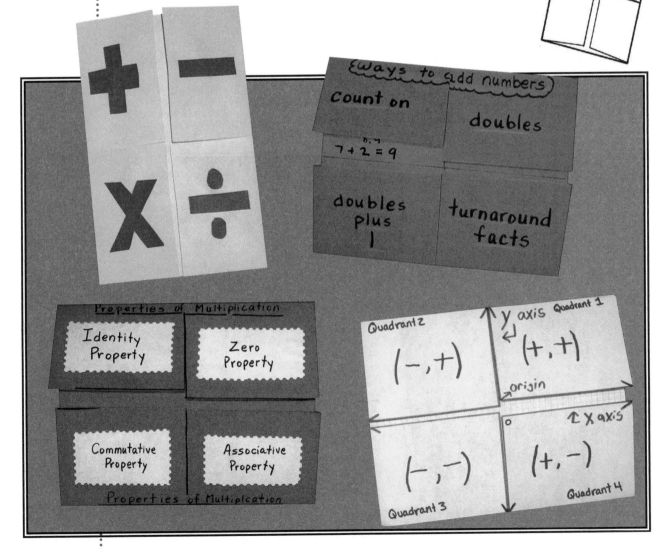

Envelope Fold

1. Fold a sheet of paper (8 1/2" χ 11") into a taco forming a square. Cut off the excess paper strip formed by the square.

2. Open the folded taco and refold it the opposite way forming another taco and an X fold pattern.

3. Open the taco fold and fold the corners toward the center point of the X forming a small square.

4. Trace this square on another sheet of paper. Cut and glue it to the inside of the envelope. Pictures can be placed under or on top of the tabs, or can be used to teach fractional parts.

Use this book for data occurring in fours. For example: the four-step problem solving process.

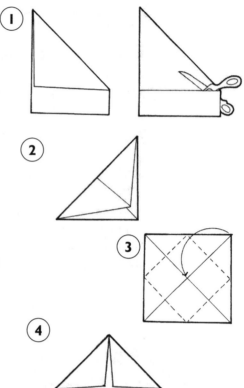

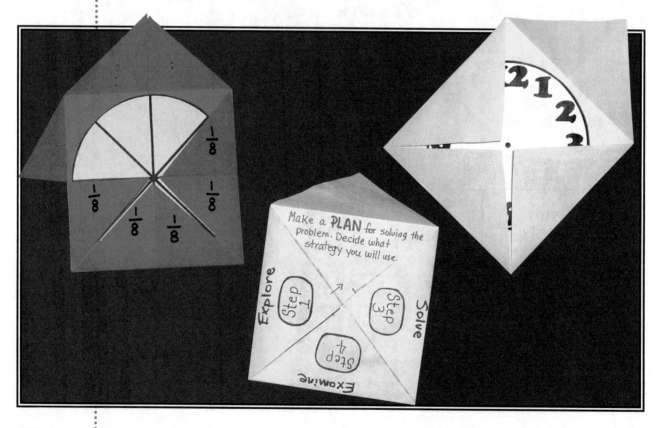

Layered-Look Book

1. Stack two sheets of paper (8 1/2" χ 11") so that the back sheet is one inch higher than the front sheet.

2. Bring the bottom of both sheets upward and align the edges so that all of the layers or tabs are the same distance apart.

3. When all tabs are an equal distance apart, fold the papers and crease well.

4. Open the papers and glue them together along the *valley* or inner center fold or, staple them along the mountain.

Under the tabs, students write problems, vocabulary terms, processes, questions and answers, and more.

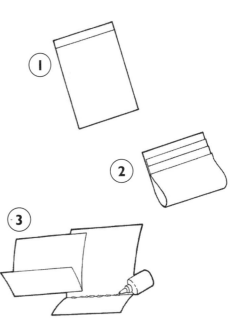

When using more than two sheets of paper, make the tabs smaller than an inch.

Top-Tab Book

1. Fold a sheet of paper (8 1/2" χ 11") in half like a *hamburger.* Cut the center fold, forming two half sheets.

2. Fold one of the half sheets four times. Begin by folding in half like a *hamburger,* fold again like a *hamburger,* and finally again like a *hamburger.* This folding has formed your pattern of four rows and four columns, or 16 small squares.

3. Fold two sheets of paper (8 1/2" χ 11") in half like a *hamburger.* Cut the center folds, forming four half sheets.

4. Hold the pattern vertically and place on a half sheet of paper under the pattern. Cut the bottom right hand square out of both sheets. Set this first page aside.

5. Take a second half sheet of paper and place it under the pattern. Cut the first and second right hand squares out of both sheets. Place the second page on top of the first page.

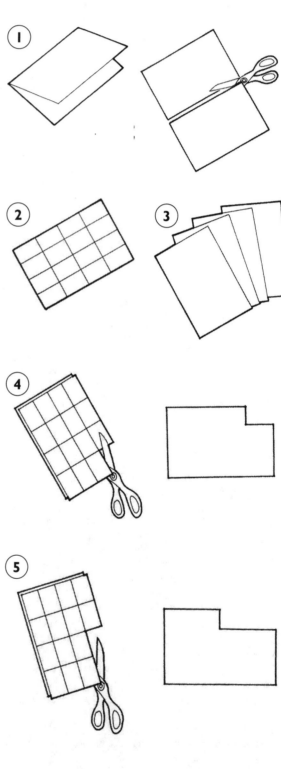

6. Take a third half sheet of paper and place it under the pattern. Cut the first, second, and third right hand squares out of both sheets. Place this third page on top of the second page.

7. Place the fourth, uncut half sheet of paper behind the three cut out sheets, leaving four aligned tabs across the top of the book. Staple several times on the left side. You can also place glue along the left paper edges, and stack them together. The glued spine is very strong.

8. Cut a final half sheet of paper with no tabs and staple along the left side to form a cover.

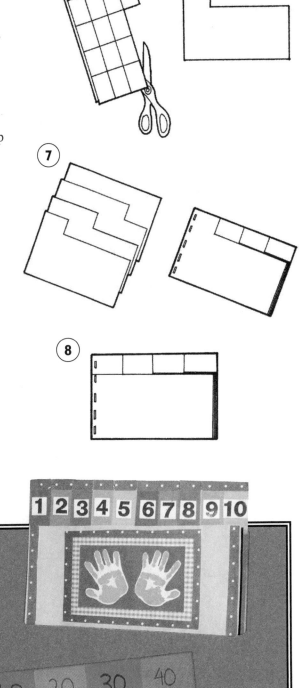

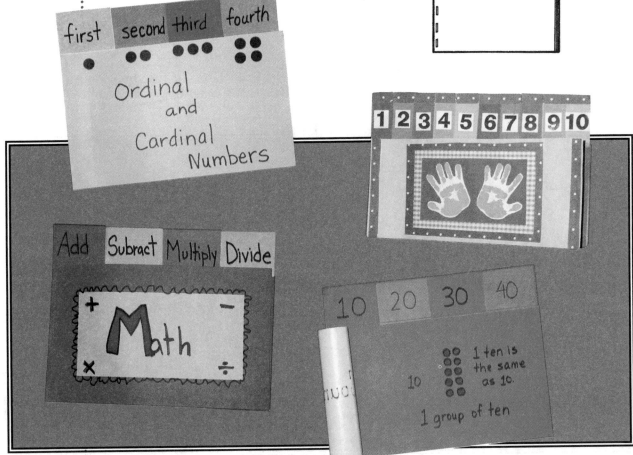

Accordion Book

NOTE: *Steps 1 and 2 should be done only if paper is too large to begin with.*

1. Fold the selected paper into *hamburgers*.

2. Cut the paper in half along the fold lines.

3. Fold each section of paper into *hamburgers*. However, fold one side one half inch shorter than the other side. This will form a tab that is one half inch long.

4. Fold this tab forward over the shorter side, and then fold it back away from the shorter piece of paper (in other words, fold it the opposite way).

5. Glue together to form an *accordion* by gluing a straight edge of one section into the *valley* of another section.

NOTE: *Stand the sections on end to form an* accordion *to help students visualize how to glue them together. (See illustration.)*

Always place the extra tab at the back of the book so you can add more pages later.

Use this book for timelines, student projects that grow, sequencing events or data, and biographies.

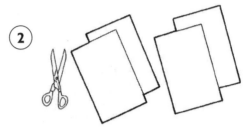

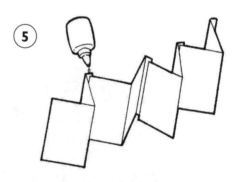

When folded, this project is used like a book, and it can be stored in student portfolios. When open, it makes a nice project display. Accordion books can be stored in file cabinets for future use, too.

Pop-Up Book

1. Fold a sheet of paper (8 1/2" χ 11") in half like a *hamburger*.

2. Beginning at the fold, or *mountain* top, cut one or more tabs.

3. Fold the tabs back and forth several times until there is a good fold line formed.

4. Partially open the *hamburger* fold and push the tabs through to the inside.

5. With one small dot of glue, glue figures for the *pop-up book* to the front of each tab. Allow the glue to dry before going on to the next step.

6. Make a cover for the book by folding another sheet of paper in half like a *hamburger*. Place glue around the outside edges of the *pop-up book* and firmly press inside the *hamburger* cover.

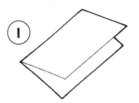
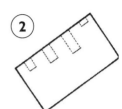
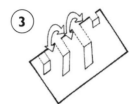
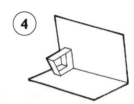

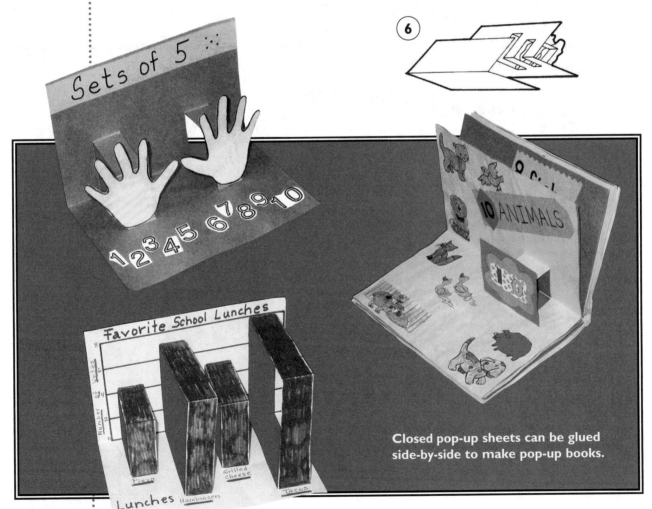

Closed pop-up sheets can be glued side-by-side to make pop-up books.

Folding into Fifths

1. Fold a sheet of paper in half like a hotdog or hamburger for a five tab book, or leave open for a folded table or chart.

2. Fold the paper so that one third is exposed and two thirds are covered.

3. Fold the two thirds section in half.

4. Fold the one third section (single thickness) backward to form a fold line.

The paper will be divided into fifths when opened.

①

②
| 1/3 | 2/3 |

③

④

.75   ½   5/10   26/100   71/100

Rename fractions as decimals...

Explain Why...

| whole numbers | integers | fractions | mixed numbers | decimals |

... are rational numbers

Monday

Tuesday

Wednesday

Thursday

Friday

one   two   three   four   five

1   2   3   4   5

Edge
a line segment where two faces of a 3-D figure meet

edge

| Base | Vertex | Face | | Net |

MATH WORDS Define and Diagram:

Folded Table or Chart

1. Fold the number of vertical columns needed to make the table or chart.

2. Fold the horizontal rows needed to make the table or chart.

3. Label the rows and columns.

Remember: Tables are organized along vertical and horizontal axes, while charts are organized along one axis, either horizontal or vertical.

Table

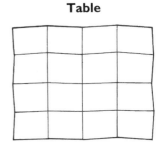

Chart

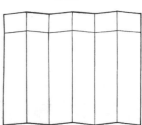

Use bulletin board paper to make giant folded tables or charts.

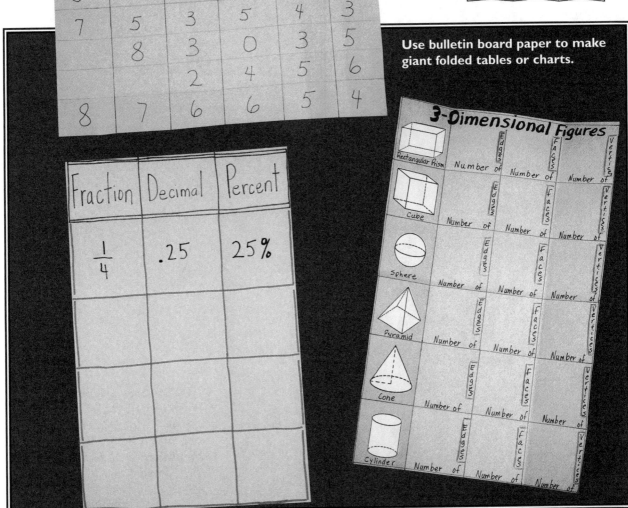

Thousands			Ones		
Hundreds	Tens	Ones	Hundreds	Tens	Ones
5	2	9	3	5	5
7	5	3	5	4	3
	8	3	0	3	5
		2	4	5	6
8	7	6	6	5	4

Fraction	Decimal	Percent
$\frac{1}{4}$	.25	25%

3-Dimensional Figures

Rectangular Prism	Number of Edges	Number of Faces	Number of Vertices
Cube	Number of Edges	Number of Faces	Number of Vertices
Sphere	Number of Edges	Number of Faces	Number of Vertices
Pyramid	Number of Edges	Number of Faces	Number of Vertices
Cone	Number of Edges	Number of Faces	Number of Vertices
Cylinder	Number of Edges	Number of Faces	Number of Vertices

Folding a Circle into Tenths

1. Fold a paper circle in half.

2. Fold the half circle so that one third is exposed and two thirds are covered.

3. Fold the one third (single thickness) backward to form a fold line.

4. Fold the two thirds section in half.

5. The half circle will be divided into fifths. When opened, the circle will be divided into tenths.

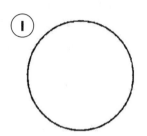

2/3

1/3

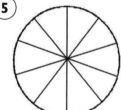

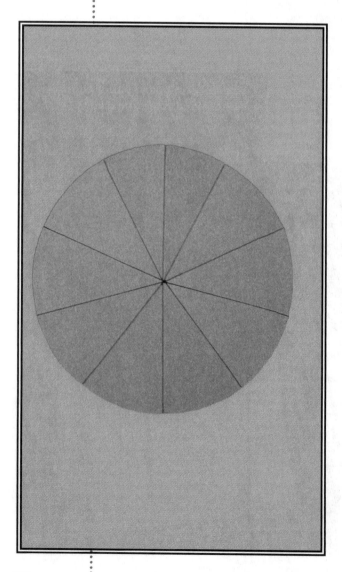

NOTE: *Paper squares and rectangles are folded into tenths the same way. Fold them so that one third is exposed and two thirds is covered. Continue with steps 3 and 4.*

Circle Graph

1. Cut out two circles using a pattern.

2. Fold one of the circles in half on each axis, forming fourths. Cut along one of the fold lines (the radius) to the middle of each circle. Flatten the circle.

3. Slip the two circles together along the cuts until they overlap completely.

4. Spin one of the circles while holding the other stationary. Estimate how much of each of the two (or you can add more) circles should be exposed to illustrate given percentages or fractional parts of data. Add circles to represent more than two percentages.

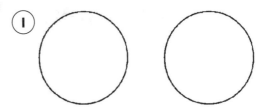

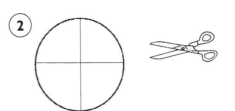

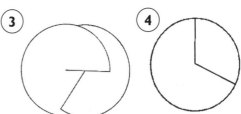

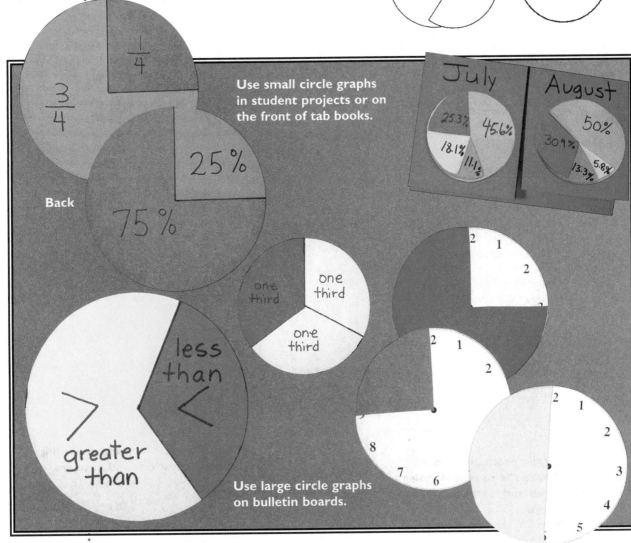

Use small circle graphs in student projects or on the front of tab books.

Use large circle graphs on bulletin boards.

Vocabulary Book

1. Fold a sheet of notebook paper in half like a *hotdog*.

2. On one side, cut every third line. This results in ten tabs on wide ruled notebook paper and twelve tabs on college ruled.

3. Label the tabs.

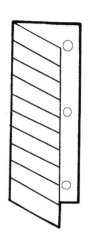
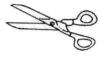

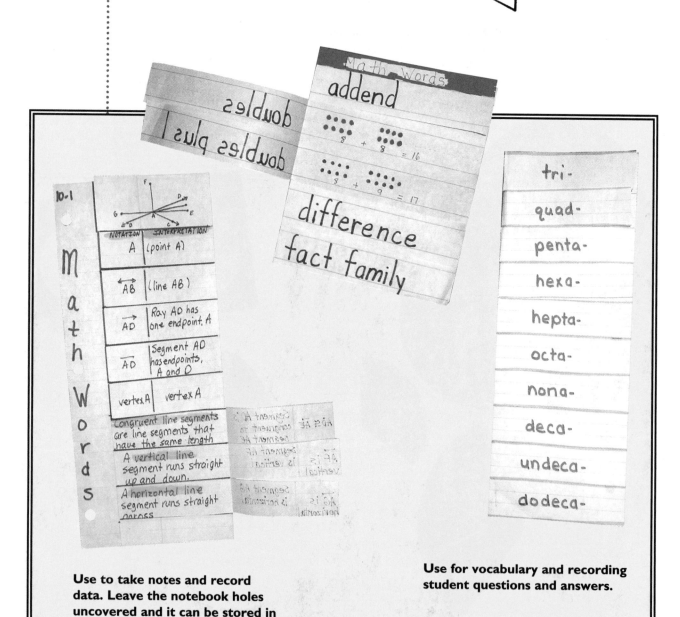

Use to take notes and record data. Leave the notebook holes uncovered and it can be stored in a notebook.

Use for vocabulary and recording student questions and answers.

Concept-Map Book

1. Fold a sheet of paper along the long or short axis, leaving a two-inch tab uncovered along the top.

2. Fold in half or in thirds.

3. Unfold and cut along the two or three inside fold lines.

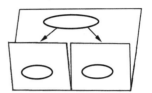

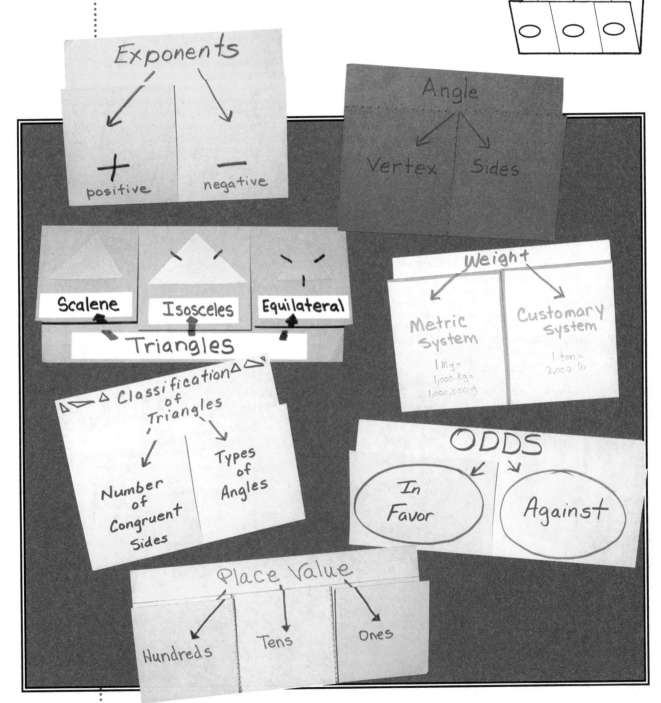

Four-Door Diorama

1. Make a *four-door book* out of a *shutter fold.*

2. Fold the two inside corners back to the outer edges (*mountains*) of the *shutter fold.* This will result in two *tacos* that will make the *four-door book* look like it has a shirt collar. Do the same thing to the bottom of the *four-door book.* When finished, four small triangular *tacos* have been made.

3. Form a 90-degree angle and overlap the folded triangles to make a display case that doesn't use staples or glue. (It can be collapsed for storage.)

4. Or, as illustrated, cut off all four triangles, or *tacos.* Staple or glue the sides.

Glue display cases end-to-end to compare and contrast or to sequence events or data.

Use 11" x 17" paper to make a large display case.

Use poster board to make giant display cases.

Display Case

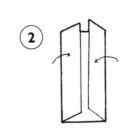

1. Make a *taco* fold and cut off the rectangular tab formed. This will result in a square.

2. Fold the square into a *shutter fold*.

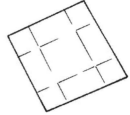

3. Unfold and fold the square into another *shutter fold* perpendicular to the direction of the first. This will form a small square at each of the four corners of the sheet of paper.

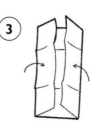

4. As illustrated, cut along two fold lines on opposite sides of the large square.

5. Collapse in and glue the cut tabs to form an open box.

How to Make a Lid

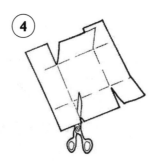

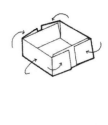

Fold another open-sided box using a square of paper one half inch larger than the square used to make the first box. This will make a lid that fits snugly over the display box. *Example:* If the base is made out of an 8 1/2" paper square, then make the top out of a 9" square.

Cut a hole out of the lid and cover the opening with a cut piece of acetate used on overhead projectors. Heavy, clear plastic wrap or scraps from a laminating machine also will work. Secure the clear plastic sheet to the inside of the lid with glue or tape.

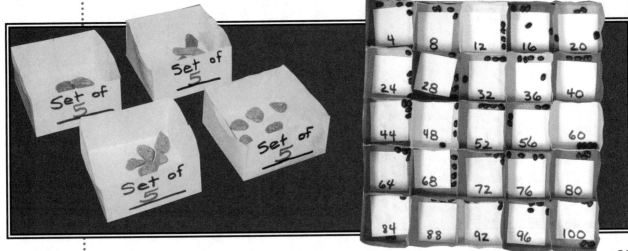

Project Board with Tabs

1. Draw a large illustration or a series of small illustrations or write on the front of one of the pieces of selected-size paper.

2. Pinch and slightly fold the paper at the point where a tab is desired on the illustrated project board. Cut into the paper on the fold. Cut straight in, then cut up to form an "L." When the paper is unfolded, it will form a tab with an illustration on the front.

3. After all tabs have been cut, glue this front sheet onto a second piece of paper. Place glue around all four edges and in the middle, away from tabs.

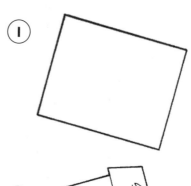

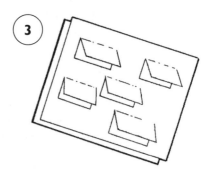

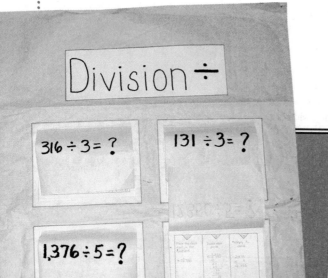

Write or draw under the tabs. If the project is made as a bulletin board using butcher paper, quarter and half-sheets of paper can be glued under the tabs.

Billboard Project

1. Fold all pieces of the same size of paper in half like *hamburgers*.

2. Place a line of glue at the top and bottom of one side of each folded billboard section and glue them edge-to-edge on a background paper or project board. If glued correctly, all doors will open from right to left.

3. Pictures, dates, words, etc., go on the front of each billboard section. When opened, writing or drawings can be seen on the inside left of each section. The base, or the part glued to the background, is perfect for more in-depth information or definitions.

Use for timelines, numberlines, or sequencing data.

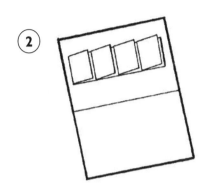

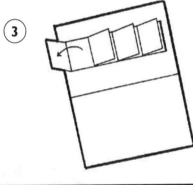

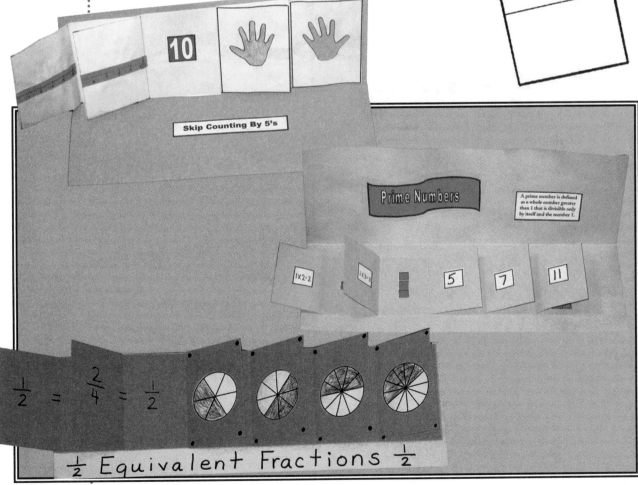

Sentence Strips

1. Take two sheets of paper (8 1/2" x 11") and fold into hamburgers. Cut along the fold lines making four half sheets. *(Use as many half sheets as necessary for additional pages to your book.)*

2. Fold each sheet in half like a hotdog.

3. Place the folds side-by-side and staple them together on the left side.

4. 1" from the stapled edge, cut the front page of each folded section up to the mountain top. These cuts form flaps that can be raised and lowered.

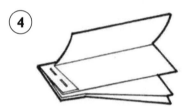

To make a half-cover, use a sheet of construction paper one inch longer than the book. Glue the back of the last sheet to the construction paper strip leaving one inch, on the left side, to fold over and cover the original staples. Staple this half-cover in place.

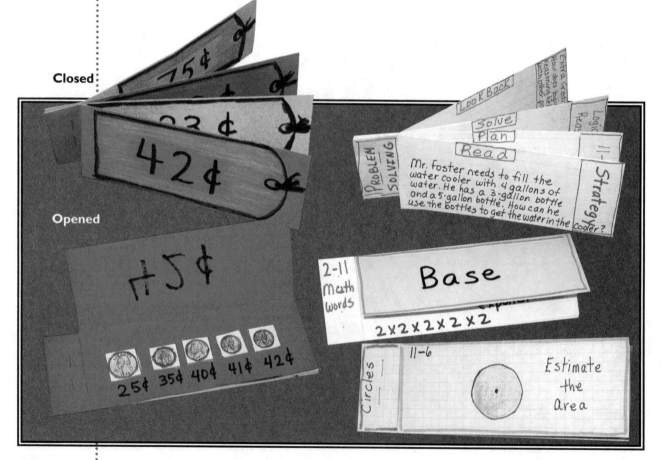

Closed

Opened

Sentence-Strip Holder

1. Fold a sheet of paper (8 1/2" χ 11") in half like a *hamburger.*

2. Open the *hamburger* and fold the two outer edges toward the *valley.* This forms a *shutter fold.*

3. Fold one of the inside edges of the shutter back to the outside fold. This fold forms a floppy "L."

4. Glue the floppy L-tab down to the base so that it forms a strong, straight L-tab.

5. Glue the other shutter side to the front of this L-tab. This forms a tent that is the backboard for the flashcards or student work to be displayed.

6. Fold the edge of the L-tab up one quarter to one half to form a lip that will keep the student work from slipping off the holder.

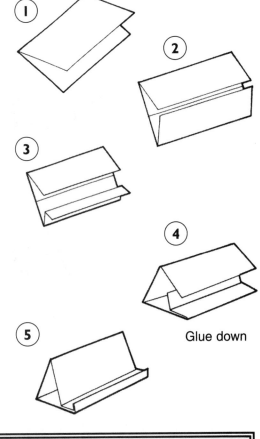

Glue down

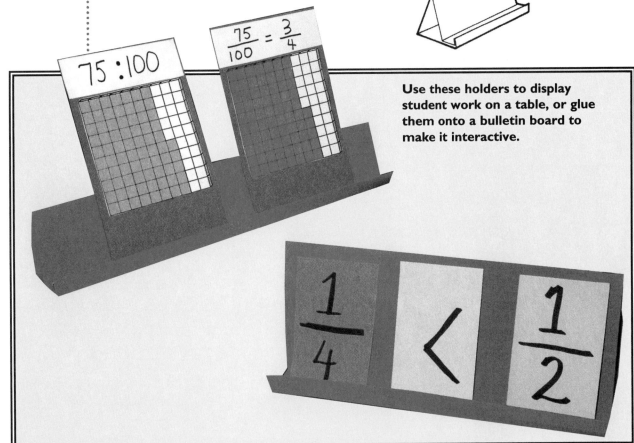

Use these holders to display student work on a table, or glue them onto a bulletin board to make it interactive.

Math Activities
Using
Foldables

General Topics

The following Math topics are covered in this section.

Problem Solving

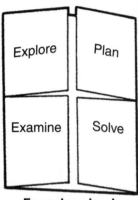

Problem Solving

K	
LK	
L	

Layer book
(2 sheets of paper)

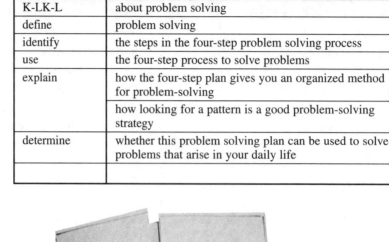

Skill	Activity Suggestion	Foldable Parts
K-LK-L	about problem solving	3
define	problem solving	1
identify	the steps in the four-step problem solving process	4
use	the four-step process to solve problems	4
explain	how the four-step plan gives you an organized method for problem-solving	1
	how looking for a pattern is a good problem-solving strategy	1
determine	whether this problem solving plan can be used to solve problems that arise in your daily life	any number

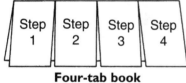

Explore	Plan
Examine	Solve

Four-door book

Step 1	Step 2	Step 3	Step 4

Four-tab book

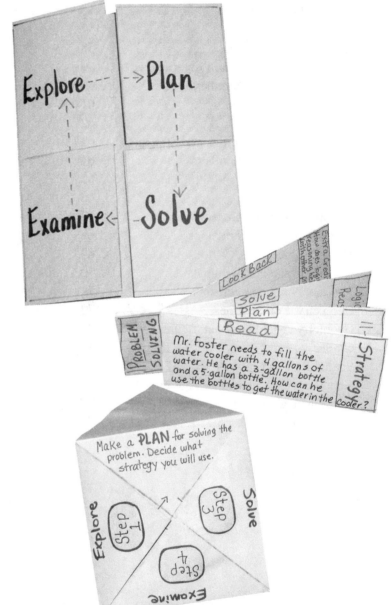

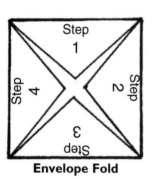

Envelope Fold

History of Counting Numbers

Skill	Activity Suggestion	Foldable Parts
describe	the purpose of a numeration system in your own words: • a method of counting • a method of communicating quantities • a method of recording quantities	3
use	tally marks to record the number of objects in three or more sets	3+
	tally marks to develop a system of numeration and explain your system so it could be used by others	2
discuss	the importance of having an agreed upon, or standard, set of symbols and a standard method for using these symbols	2
define	the following: • *number* as a way in which to describe and discuss quantity • *numerals* as the symbols used to write numbers • *numeration system* as a method of naming numbers	3
outline	the steps one might go through to develop a numeration system: • develop a set of symbols • assign a value to each symbol • outline ways to combine the values of more than one symbol • outline ways to take away the value of one symbol from the value of another symbol	any number
research	the what, where, when, why/how of the following ancient numeration systems: • Babylonian Numeration System • Egyptian Numeration System • Chinese Numeration System • Indian Numeration System • Inca Numeration System • Greek Numeration System • Roman Numeration System • Hindu-Arabic Numeration System	4
	different sets of symbols used in the distant past to represent numbers	any number
compare	an addition numeration system (ex. Egyptian system) and a multiplication numeration system (ex. Chinese system)	2

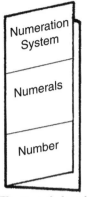

Three-tab book

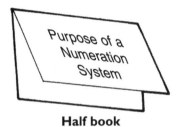

Half book

Standard Systems	
Pros	Cons

1x2 Chart

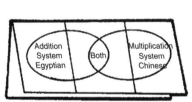

Three-tab Venn diagram

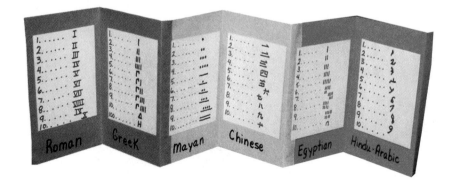

Roman Numerals

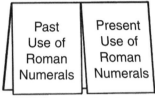

Number	Roman Numeral

1x2 Chart

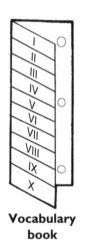

| | | Past Use of Roman Numerals | Present Use of Roman Numerals |

Two-tab book

I
II
III
IV
V
VI
VII
VIII
IX
X

Vocabulary book

Skill	Activity Suggestion	Foldable Parts
K-LK-L	about Roman numerals	3
tell	why you think the Roman numeration system is the only ancient system still used today	1
debate	the value of the Roman system in today's world	1
describe	Roman numerals	1
write	Roman numerals to 10	10
	the number that a Roman numeral stands for	any number
	six given numbers as Roman numerals	6
	your age and the ages of three other people in Roman numerals	4
use	Roman numerals to write the current year and two other years	3
list	even and odd numbers written as Roman numerals	2
show	how to add to find the value of II, III, VI, XX	4
determine	the value of a Roman numeral by adding or subtracting	2
explain	how to find the value of a Roman numeral when a letter of less value is right of a letter of greater value: VI and XI	2
	how to find the value of a Roman numeral when more than one letter of less value is right of a letter of greater value: VIII and XII	2
	how to find the value of a Roman numeral when a letter of less value is left of a letter of greater value: IX and IV	2
solve	three addition problems using Roman numerals	3
	three subtraction problems using Roman numerals	3
differentiate	between IX and XI between IV and VI between LX and XL	3
compare and contrast	Roman numerals and the number system used today	2
compare	the use of Roman numerals past and present	2
speculate	as to why zero was not used in the Roman numeration system	1
make	a time line of key events occurring in your life and use Roman numerals for the dates	any number
	a hundreds chart using Roman numerals	100
show and explain	two ways to write the number 999: IM or DCCCIC	2

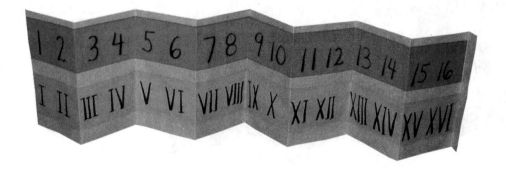

Whole Numbers or Counting Numbers

Skill	Activity Suggestion	Foldable Parts
K-LK-L	about whole numbers (also called counting numbers or natural numbers)	3
define	the word "digit" as a symbol used to write numbers	1
describe	why counting numbers are also called whole numbers 0, 1, 2, 3, 4, 5, 6, ...	1
count, read, write	• numbers from 1 to 10 • numbers from 1 to 20 • numbers from 1 to 50 • numbers from 1 to 100 • numbers from 1 to 1,000 • numbers from 1 to 100, 000 • numbers from 1 to 1,000, 000 and beyond	any number
write	the word names for the following numbers: • numbers from 1 to 10 • numbers from 1 to 20 • numbers from 1 to 50 • numbers from 1 to 100 • numbers from 1 to 1000 • numbers from 1 to 100,000 • numbers from 1 to 1,000,000 and beyond	any number
determine	how many objects in any given set: dishes, crayons, candy, coins, books, others	any number
recognize	sets of 2, 3, 4, 5, 6, 7, 8, 9, or 10 objects in varying patterns, or arrays, without counting	any number
count	the number of objects in a set and determine by regrouping whether the set can be divided into two equal parts, three equal parts, or four equal parts	3
explain	the purpose of 0 in your own words	1
	why the following fractions are whole numbers: 3/3, 8/8, and 19/19	3
write	descriptively about a million and a billion	2
use	large numbers to report populations of cities, states, countries, and the world	4
report	on two things that exist in large numbers: stars, germs, molecules, grains of sand, others	2
	on something that costs a lot of money: buying a house, payroll of a company, travel, others	1
prove	that subtraction and division are the opposite, or inverse, operations of addition and multiplication	2
use	whole numbers to solve 3 real-life problems	3
make a flow chart	and give examples that show progression through the following counting stages: • rote counting: say number names in order • rational counting: determine the number of objects by counting • comparison counting: numbers are used to show differences in size, time, quantity, weight, distance (ex. find numbers smaller than 6) • reproduction counting: select a given number of objects from a larger set of objects (ex. place four blocks on the table, make a set of 5 pencils) • grouping: the association of a number with a set of objects (ex. a set of 2 and a set of 4 combines to form a set of 6 objects)	5

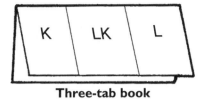

Three-tab book

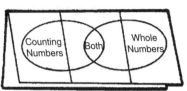

Three-tab Venn diagram

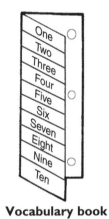

Vocabulary book

Half book

Two-tab concept map

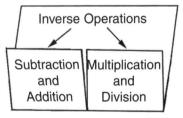

Ordinal and Cardinal Numbers

Ordinal	Cardinal
6	sixth
12	twelfth
30	thirtieth
1	first
43	forty-third
11	eleventh

1x2 Chart

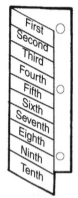

Vocabulary book

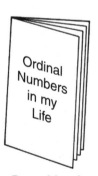

Bound book

Skill	Activity Suggestion	Foldable Parts
K-LK-L	about ordinal and cardinal numbers	3
describe	ordinal numbers as numbers that tell order or position and give examples of how they are used as adjectives	2
Venn diagram	ordinal numbers, cardinal numbers, both	3
write and read	ordinal numbers: • numbers to 10 • numbers to 20 • numbers to 50 • numbers to 100	any number
explain	ordinal and cardinal numbers using a calendar	2
	ordinal and cardinal numbers as they relate to rows and seats in an auditorium	2
	ordinal and cardinal numbers as they relate to the numbering and naming of pages in a book	2
describe	ordinal numbers as they relate to the following: • prizes • positions in a line • ranking sports teams • grade levels • street names	5
list	ways in which you hear ordinal numbers used in a given period of time: 1 television show, 1 day, 1 week	any number
give	three examples of numbers with exponents and explain how ordinal numbers are used when reading exponents: • 10^3, 10 to the third power • 4^2, 4 to the second power • 7^4, 7 to the fourth power	3
	three examples of fractions and explain how ordinal numbers are used when reading each fractions	3
play a game	to locate objects explained by ordinal numbers: • touch the third number • point to the fifth house on the block • pick up the seventh book, others	any number

Prime and Composite Numbers

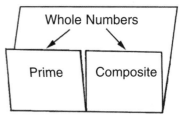

Skill	Activity Suggestion	Foldable Parts
K-LK-L	about prime and composite numbers	3
define and explain	prime numbers as whole numbers greater than one that that have exactly two factors, one and itself	2
	prime numbers as prime integers	1
	composite numbers as whole numbers greater than one that have more than two factors	2
list	5 prime numbers and explain why they are prime	5
	5 composite numbers and list the factors of each	5
compare and contrast	two types of whole or counting numbers: primes and composites	2
differentiate	between prime and composite numbers	2
Venn diagram	characteristics of prime numbers, composite numbers, both	3
make	a table of numbers to 100 and mark the prime and composite numbers	2
mark	prime and composite numbers on a number line using two different colors of markers	2
explain why	0 and 1 are neither prime nor composite	2
prove	every whole number greater than 1 is either prime or composite	1
use	prime factorization to find the greatest common factor, or GCF, of 6 numbers	6
determine	how many even primes there are	1
	if the set of all primes excluding 2, are odd numbers	1

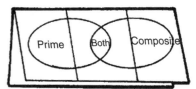

Two-tab concept map

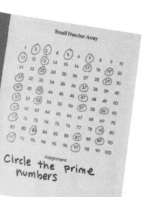

Three-tab Venn diagram

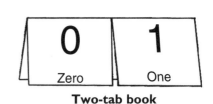

1x3 Chart

Closed

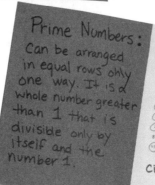

Two-tab book

Opened

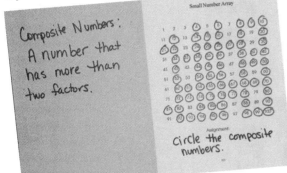

Composite Numbers: A number that has more than two factors.

Circle the composite numbers.

Prime Numbers: Can be arranged in equal rows only one way. It is a whole number greater than 1 that is divisible only by itself and the number 1.

Circle the prime numbers

Factors

Skill	Activity Suggestion	Foldable Parts
K-LK-L	about factors and factorization, or factoring	3
define	factors in terms of division and multiplication: • division: factors are the numbers that divide a whole number with a remainder of 0 • multiplication: factors are portions of a number that can be multiplied by all other portions to give the entire number.	2
use	the phrase "divisible by" when describing the factors of a given number	1
determine	whether one number is a factor of another	any number
explain	how even and odd numbers relate to factors	2
	why 1 is a factor of every nonzero number	1
find	factors of four given numbers	4
list	numbers with exactly 2, 3, or 4 factors	3
	the factors of 1	1
describe	greatest common factor, or GCF, and give an example	2
	the greatest common factor of two numbers as the greatest factor these numbers have in common	1
calculate	the GCF of two numbers	1

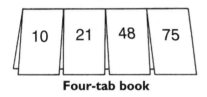

#	Factors
1	1
2	1,2
3	1,3
4	1,2,4
5	1,5
6	1,2,3,6
7	1,7

1x2 Chart

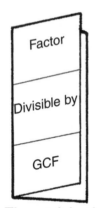

10	21	48	75

Four-tab book

Factor

Divisible by

GCF

Three-tab book

#	#	GCF
10	25	5

1x3 Chart

Rounding Numbers

Skill	Activity Suggestion	Foldable Parts
K-LK-L	about rounding numbers	3
define	the term "round" as finding the nearest value of a number based on approximating or based on a given set of guidelines	1
round	five numbers up	5
	five numbers down	5
	four numbers to the nearest ten	4
	four numbers to the nearest hundred	4
	three numbers to the nearest thousand	3
	three numbers to the nearest hundred thousand	3
explain	how to use rounding to add and subtract	2
demonstrate	how rounding can aid in rapid addition and subtraction calculations	2
	how rounding can aid in rapid multiplication and division calculations	2
research	round off error and give two modern examples of errors caused by rounding	2
list	situations when rounding could and could not be used	2

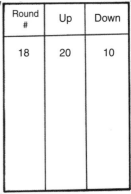

Round #	Up	Down
18	20	10

1x3 Chart

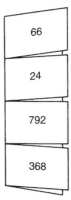

66

24

792

368

Four-tab book

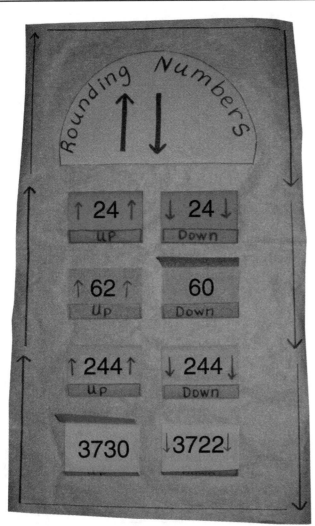

#'s	Round to nearest 100

1x2 Chart

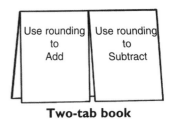

Use rounding to Add	Use rounding to Subtract

Two-tab book

Place Value

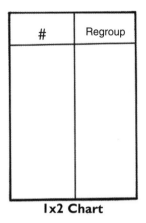

1x2 Chart

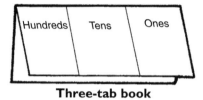

Three-tab book

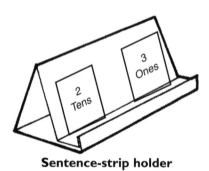

Sentence-strip holder

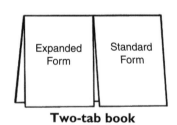

Two-tab book

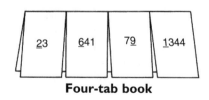

Four-tab book

Skill	Activity Suggestion	Foldable Parts
K-LK-L	about place value	3
explain	the purpose of place value	1
	place value as the basic structure of the decimal numeration system	1
	and demonstrate the use of zero as a place holder	2
place	any number of objects into as many sets of ten as possible	any number
note	every place-value numeration system has a way of grouping called its *base* and the base for the system we use is 10	2
show	how it is possible to use any number as a base to build a numeration system and the number of digits used in a system is equal to the base	2
make	a place value chart for ones and tens	2
	tables to show: • ten more than a given number • one thousand more than a given number • ten thousand more than a given number	any number
use	place value models to: • show numbers to tens • show numbers to hundreds • show numbers to thousands • show numbers to hundred thousands	any number
regroup	to rename 10 numbers *example:* • 13 ones = 1 ten and 3 ones • 134 ones = 1 hundred, 1 three tens, and four ones	10
define	"period" as groups of three digits separated by commas	1
use	place value charts to show ones, tens, hundreds	3
	place value blocks to show ones, tens, hundreds	3
	place value bundles to show ones, tens, hundreds	3
write	5 numbers using words and symbols	5
	4 numbers in expanded form *example:* • 3,000 + 200 + 50 + 9	4
	4 expanded numbers in standard form	4
	the word name for 5 expanded form numbers	5
compare	an expanded form number and a standard form number	2
explain	how expanded form shows the value of each digit	1
show	3 numbers using place value models two ways *example:* • 188 = 1 hundred, eight tens, eight ones • 152 = 15 tens and two ones	3
name	the digit in the tens place of five given numbers	5
	the digit in the hundreds place of five given numbers	5
	the digit in the thousands place of five given numbers	5
write	four numbers, underline one digit and write about the value of the underlined digit	4
	underline one digit in 3 numbers you see in print and tell the value of the underlined digits	3
research	the history and use of the abacus and explain how abaci were used by the Chinese and Romans	2
make a model	of an abacus	1

Place Value: Exponents

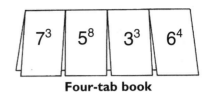

Four-tab book

Skill	Activity Suggestion	Foldable Parts
K-LK-L	about exponents	3
label and describe	the base and exponent of four numbers and give the value of each	4
write	in words how three exponents are read *example:* • 3^4, 3 to the fourth power • 5^3, 5 to the third power • 10^5, 10 to the fifth power	3
prove	that each place-value position has a value 10 times greater than the position to its right and 1/10 of the value of the position to its left	2
demonstrate	how place value is expressed through the use of exponents	1
explain	how an exponent expresses the power of a numeral	1
make a chart	to show the following as exponents: • $1 = 1 \times 10^0$ • $10 = 1 \times 10^1$ • $100 = 10 \times 10 = 10^2$ • $1000 = 10 \times 10 \times 10 = 10^3$ • $10,000 = 10 \times 10 \times 10 \times 10 = 10^4$ • $100,000 = 10 \times 10 \times 10 \times 10 \times 10 = 10^5$	6
show	four numbers in expanded notation *example:* • 6,542 • 6,000 + 500 + 40 + 2 • (6 x 1000) + (5 x 100) + (4 x 10) + (2 x 1) • $(6 \times 10^3) + (5 \times 10^2) + (4 \times 10^1) + (2 \times 10^0)$	4
	four decimals in the following manner *example:* • 4 thousandths • .004 • 4 x 1/1,000 • $4 \times 1/10^3$	4
make	a chart to illustrate how exponential notation and place value are related	2
explain	how to add and subtract numbers with the same exponents	2
	how to multiply two numbers with different exponents and how to divide two numbers with different exponents	2

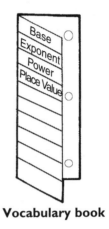

Vocabulary book

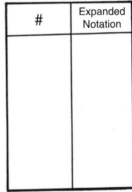

1x2 Chart

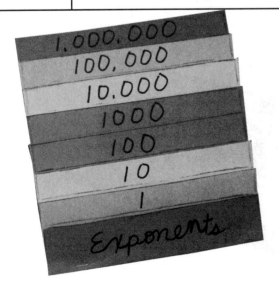

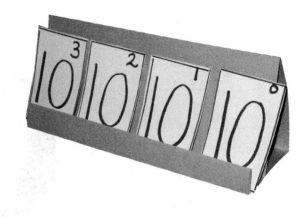

Compare Numbers

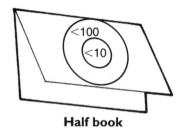

Half book

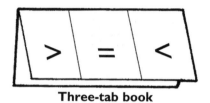

Three-tab book

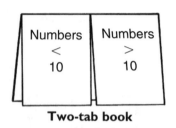

Two-tab book

Number	≥	Number

1x3 Chart

Numbers	>	<	=
17			
25			
32			

4x4 Folded chart

Skill	Activity Suggestion	Foldable Parts
K-LK-L	about comparing numbers	3
use	the words "greater than" to compare two numbers	1
	the words "less than" to compare two numbers	1
	the symbol for "greater than" to compare 4 sets of numbers	4
	the symbol for "less than" to compare 4 sets of numbers	4
read	6 inequalities using the words "greater than" and "less than"	6
define	inequalities as math sentences that contain greater than or less than symbols	1
compare	numbers within the following ranges: • 1 to 10 • 1 to 100 • 1 to 1000, others	any number
explain	how to compare numbers by comparing their digits and give two examples	2
name	numbers less than 10, 100, 1000, others	
	numbers greater than 10 but less than 21	10
determine	if a number is greater than or less than a given number	any number
use	a number line to determine if 5 numbers are before or after a given number	5
place	a greater than or less than symbol between 10 pairs of given numbers	10
compare	the following as appropriate to ability level: • whole numbers to millions and beyond • fractions • mixed numbers • decimals	any number
write	6 inequalities that are true	6
	6 inequalities that are false	6
record	three common things people say that correspond to inequalities	3
use	"is equal to" and "is not equal to" and give 4 examples of each	4
	"is less than or equal to" and "is greater than or equal to" and give 4examples of each	4

Order Numbers

Skill	Activity Suggestion	Foldable Parts
K-LK-L	about ordering numbers	3
order	the following: • numbers to 10, to 100, to 1000, to 10,000 • a given set of numbers least to greatest • a given set of numbers from greatest to least • numbers to 10, to 100, to 1000, to 10,000 • numbers with and without a number line	any number
skip count	by 2's, by 5's, and by 10's	3
	by 3's, by 4's, 6's, 7's, 8's, and by 9's	6
	with and without a number line	2
	backwards using a number line	1
	by 100's to 1,000,000	1
	by 2's, 3's, 4's, 5's, 6's, 7's, 8's, 9's, 10's beginning with any given number	9
find	missing numbers in 10 skip-counting patterns	10
use	a hundreds chart to count by 2's, 3's, 4's, 5's, 6's, 7's, 8's, 9's, 10's	any number
count	by 5's to 100 using hands and feet	20
	by 5's to 50 and to 100 using nickels	2
	by 5's using 5 minute intervals on a clock	12
	by 10's using dimes	10
order	numbers to millions and beyond	any number
	five fractions	5
	ten mixed numbers	10
	five decimals	5

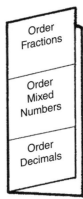

Three-tab book

Trifold book

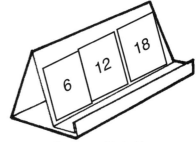

Half book

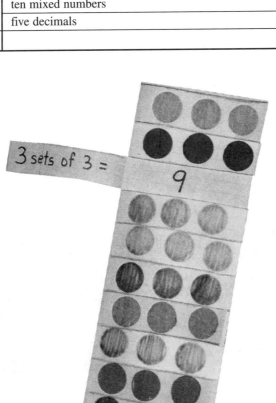

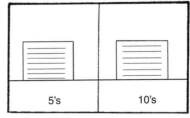

Sentence-strip holder

Pocket book

Even and Odd Numbers

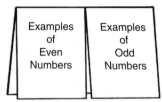

Two-tab book

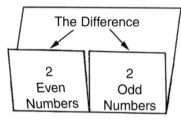

Two-tab concept map

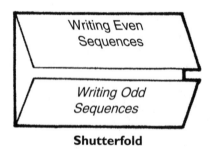

Shutterfold

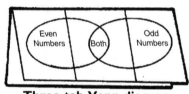

Three-tab Venn diagram

Skill	Activity Suggestion	Foldable Parts
K-LK-L	about even and odd numbers	3
describe	even and odd numbers	2
list	ten examples of even numbers and 5 examples of 5 numbers	10
describe and give examples that show	the following: • the difference of two odd numbers (even) • the difference of two even numbers (even) • the difference of an even and an odd number (odd) • the sum of two odd numbers (even) • the sum of two even numbers (even) • the sum of an even and an odd number (odd)	6
explain	the four ways to get an even number	4
	the two ways to get an odd number	2
demonstrate	that it is the ones place that determines if a number will be even or odd using 4 examples	4
describe and give examples that show	the following: • the product of two odd factors will be odd • the product of two even factors will be even • the product of an even and odd factor will be even • the quotient of an odd divisor and dividend will be odd • the quotient of an even divisor and dividend can be either even or odd	5
tell	how even and odd numbers relate to factors (remember that the factors of a whole number divide that number with a remainder of 0)	2
explain	even and odd numbers as arithmetic sequences	2
give	the next four numbers in a given even sequence	4
	the next four numbers in a given odd sequence	4
use	the pages of a book to describe even and odd numbers	2
	an egg carton to differentiate between even and odd numbers	2

Sets

Skill	Activity Suggestion	Foldable Parts
K-LK-L	about sets	3
define	the following terms: • a *set* as a collection, or grouping of objects • each object in a set is called an *element* of that set, or a *member* of the set • the *empty set* • *sets* and *subsets*	4
show	examples of sets with many elements, one element, and no elements	3
	that the number given to a set is determined by the number of elements in the set	1
	symbols for the operation of union and the operation of intersection	2
use	braces to enclose sets	any number
find	four examples of sets in the world around you and name them	4
compare	three given sets	3
complete	sets	
match	elements of two sets in one-to-one correspondence	2
join	two sets and describe set union	2
separate	sets and describe set separation	2
give	examples of equal and unequal sets	2
	two examples of sets and subsets seen in daily life	2
draw and explain	symbols to show the following relations unique to sets: • is a subset of • is not a subset of • is an element of • is not an element of • is equal to • is not equal to • is equivalent to	7
describe	in your own words when and why three dots would be used after the last element in a set	1
Venn diagram	equal sets, equivalent sets, both	3
write	four true mathematical statements about given sets	4
show	what happens when two or more sets are jointed	2+
	how diagrams can be used to illustrate sets and subsets	2
	two examples of disjoint sets or sets with no common element	2
explain	finite and infinite sets	2

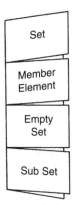

Four-tab book

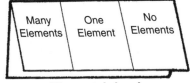

Three-tab book

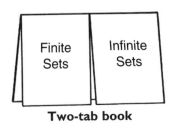

Two-tab book

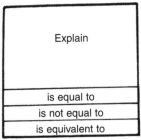

**Layer book
(2 sheets of paper)**

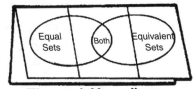

Three-tab Venn diagram

Adding Whole Numbers

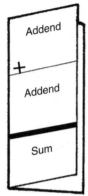

Three-tab book

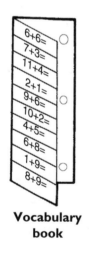

Vocabulary book

Skill	Activity Suggestion	Foldable Parts
K-LK-L	about adding whole numbers	3
describe	the operation of addition in your own words	1
define and use	the terms *addend* and *sum*	2
show and label	the addends and the sum of a problem	2
write	four addition sentences	4
list	addition problems with sums that equal the following: 2, 3, 4, 5, 6, 7, 8, 9, 10, 12, others	10+
count	up to add	any number
use	a number line to add 5 problems	5
	a place value chart to add 5 problems	5
show	how to add across and down	2
practice	addition facts with sums of 10 or less	any number
	addition facts with sums from 11 to 18	any number
	zero facts	any number
memorize	addition facts	any number
	fact families	any number
add	the following: • two single digit numbers • more than two single digit numbers • one-digit and two-digit numbers • two digit numbers with and without regrouping • three digit numbers with and without regrouping • multi-digit numbers with and without regrouping	any number
practice	solving problems mentally	any number
	solving problems with numbers in any order	any number
use	place value models to regroup tens and ones	1
	place value models to regroup hundreds and thousands	1
outline	the steps used to solve two given addition problems	2
explain	two ways to check addition problems	2
estimate	to find sums of four problems	4
round	addends of three problems to find estimated sums	3
determine	when it is appropriate and inappropriate to estimate sums	2
	the reasonableness of a sum	1
give	examples that show: • the sum of two odd numbers is even • the sum of two even number is even • the sum of an even and an odd number is odd	3
write	four addition sentences in column form	4
	four addition sentences in horizontal form	4
write and solve	three word problems using addition	3

1x3 Chart

#	Count Up	Answer
6	3	9

1x3 Chart

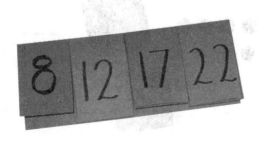

Addition: Strategies and Properties

Skill	Activity Suggestion	Foldable Parts
K-LK-L	about addition properties	3
state and	the identity property *example:* • 14 + 0 = 14	2
explain	the commutative property *example:* • 15+ 21= 36, 21+15 = 36	2
	the associative property *example:* • 15+5+2= add 15+5 add 2 to the sum to get 22 • add 5 + 2 and then add 15 to the sum to get 22	2
	how each of these properties can help you add mentally	3
use	models to illustrate the following properties: • identity property • commutative property • associative property	3
describe	when to use parenthesis to group addends and give three examples	3
	inverse operations and give examples *example:* • addition is the inverse operation of subtraction 5 - 3 = 2 so 2 + 3 = 5 • subtraction is the inverse operation of addition 3 + 2 = 5 so 5 - 2 = 3	2
prove	when whole numbers are added, the sum is always a whole number	1

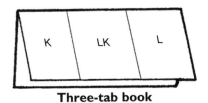

Three-tab book

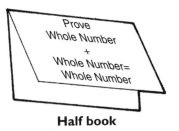

Half book

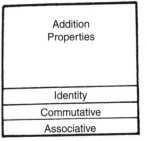

Layer book
(2 sheets of paper)

Explain:
5−3=2
5−2=3

Explain:
3+2=5
2+3=5

Two-tab book

Equation | Inverse Operation

6+9=15 | 15-6=9
10-5=5 | 5+5=10

Subtracting Whole Numbers

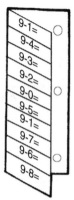

Vocabulary book

Three-tab book

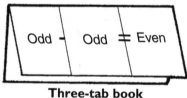

Three-tab book

Hundreds	to Tens
200	20
450	45

1x2 Chart

Skill	Activity Suggestion	Foldable Parts
K-LK-L	about subtracting whole numbers	3
describe	the operation of subtraction in your own words	1
define and use	the terms *minuend, subtrahend,* and *differences*	3
show and label	the *minuend, subtrahend,* and *difference* of a problem	3
write	four subtraction sentences	4
subtract	from each of the following numbers: • 3, 4, 5, 6, 7, 8, 9, 10, others • 1-digit numbers from 2-digit numbers with and without regrouping • 2-digit numbers from 2-digit numbers with and without regrouping • 2-digit numbers from 3-digit numbers • 3-digit numbers from 3-digit numbers	any number
write	the following: • addition and subtraction fact families • related facts or basic facts from a fact family • subtraction sentences across and down	any number
find	missing addends	any number
check	two subtraction problems using addition	2
estimate	four subtraction differences	4
round	three numbers to find estimated differences	3
relate	addition and subtraction	2
use	patterns to find differences mentally	any number
	a number line to subtract	any number
prove	the following: • the difference of two odd numbers is even • the difference of two even numbers is even • the difference of an even and an odd number is odd	3
explain	why a difference seems to be reasonable	1
	why it is impossible to solve some subtraction problems unless their form is changed, and make a chart to show 3 examples • titles for chart columns: *example, regrouped form, explanation*	3
recognize	that ones in subtrahend cannot be subtracted from ones in the minuend if the ones in the subtrahend are greater than ones in the minuend	1
	that the tens in the subtrahend cannot be subtracted from tens in the minuend if the tens in the subtrahend are greater than the tens in the minuend	1
practice	the following: • changing tens to ones • changing hundreds to tens • changing thousands to hundreds • changing tens to ones and hundreds to tens • changing hundreds to tens and thousands to hundreds	5
regroup	across a zero and outline the thought process used	2
teach	someone how to subtract with regrouping	1
subtract	whole numbers of 5 or more digits	any number

Subtraction Experiences

Skill	Activity Suggestion	Foldable Parts
find	*how many are left*, or the remainder *example:* • 5 cookies in a bowl and two where eaten • 6 birds in a tree and two flew away	any number
compare	numbers to find *how many more or less*, or the difference *example:* • 5 cookies in a bowl, 8 in another bowl, *how many more (or less)* cookies in one bowl than the other?	any number
determine	*how many more are needed* to find the difference between the number present and the number needed *example:* • 5 cookies in a bowl, how many more are needed to have 10 cookies in the bowl	any number
make	change, or find the difference between the purchase price and the amount of money given in payment *example:* • 5 cookies cost $1.25, *how much change* will be given from $2.00?	any number
write	word problems to illustrate the following: • take 3 away from 7 • from 9, take 6 away • subtract 7 from 21 • 15 minus 4	4
	word problems to illustrate the following: • how many more are there in 23 than in 12? • how many less (fewer) are there in 10 than in 20? • how much more is 50 than 30? • find the number less in 12 than in 46 • what is the difference between 33 and 13? • compare 27 things with 12 things • 229 minus 26	any number
check	five subtraction problems using addition	5
estimate	differences to three subtraction problems that arise in daily life	3

Have	Need	How Many More
8	20	12
12	20	8
3	15	12

1x3 Chart

Folded book
(using a worksheet)

Subtraction Problem	Addition Check

1x2 Chart

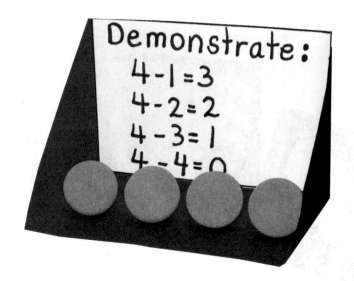

Take 3 Away From 7	From 9 Take 6 Away	Subtract 7 From 21	15 minus 4

Four-tab book

Multiplication

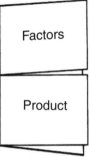

Factors

Product

Two-tab book

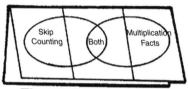

| Skip Counting | Both | Multiplication Facts |

Three-tab Venn diagram

Problem	Estimate	Solution

1x3 Chart

Skill	Activity Suggestion	Foldable Parts
K-LK-L	about the operation of multiplication	3
describe	the operation of multiplication in your own words	1
define and use	the terms "factor" and "product"	2
show and label	the factors and the product of a multiplication problem	2
write	four multiplication sentences	4
use	models to find 4 products *example:* • 3 groups of 6 • 7 groups of 2, others	4
draw	2 pictures and write multiplication sentences for them	2
make	a chart to show number of groups, number of items in each group, and total number of items	3
	a multiplication table	
relate	skip counting and multiplication facts	2
	multiplication and addition	2
find	patterns in a multiplication table	any number
use	repeated addition to solve 4 multiplication problems	4
	a number line to multiply and find four products	4
	models to multiply tens	any number
find	6 products by adding onto known multiplication facts	6
draw	arrays to show three multiplication problems	3
memorize	multiplication facts for factors 0-5 and 0-12	
find	the square numbers in the facts for factors 0-12	12
	missing factors in 10 multiplication problems	10
draw	four models to show square numbers	4
outline	a computation method used to find products	1
estimate	five products and check estimates	5
determine	reasonableness of a four products	4
multiply	with and without regrouping: • 1-digit by 1-digit numbers • 2-digit by 1-digit numbers • 3-digit and multi-digit numbers by 1-digit numbers • 2-digit by 2-digit numbers • 2-digit by multi-digit numbers • 3-digit by 3-digit numbers	any number

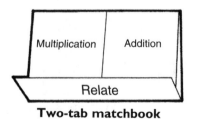

| Multiplication | Addition |

Relate

Two-tab matchbook

Multiplication: Properties and Strategies

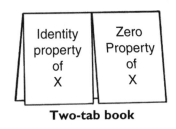

Two-tab book

Skill	Activity Suggestion	Foldable Parts
K-LK-L	about the properties of multiplication	3
state and	the identity property of multiplication *example:* • 4 x 1 = 4	2
explain	the zero property *example:* • 5 x 0 = 0	2
	the commutative property *example:* • 3 x 6 = 18, 6 x 3 = 18	2
	the associative property: *example:* 2 x 5 x 3= • multiply 2 x 5, then multiply 10 x 3 to get 30 • multiply 5 x 3, then multiply 15 x 2 to get 30	2
	how each of these properties can help you multiply mentally	4
use	models to illustrate the identity property	1
	models to illustrate the commutative property	1
	models to illustrate the associative property	11
describe	when to use parenthesis to group factors and give three examples	3
explain	and use the four properties of multiplication	4

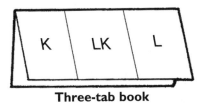

Three-tab book

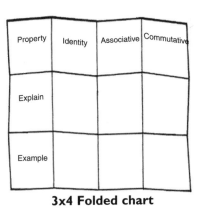

Multiplication

Identity Property
Associative Property
Commutative Property

Layer book
(2 sheets of paper)

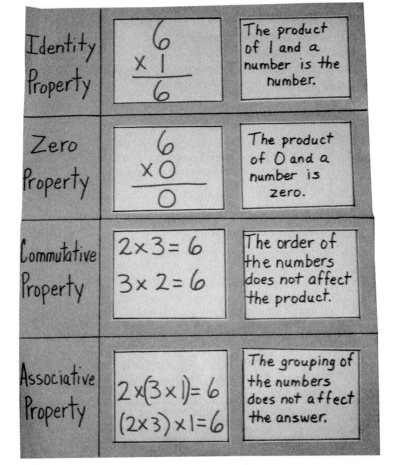

Property	Identity	Associative	Commutative
Explain			
Example			

3x4 Folded chart

Division of Whole Numbers

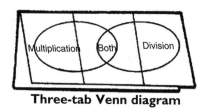

Three-tab book

Three-tab Venn diagram

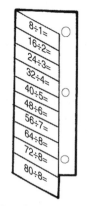

Three-tab book

Vocabulary Book

Skill	Activity Suggestion	Foldable Parts
K-LK-L	about division of whole numbers	3
describe	the operation of division in your own words	1
define and use	the terms *dividend*, *divisor*, and *quotient*	3
model	four division facts using counters or pictures	4
write	four division sentences	4
find	missing factors in 10 problems	10
use	four models to find products: *example:* • 3 groups of 6 • 7 groups of 2, others	4
draw	three pictures and write related multiplication and division sentences for each	3
show	division as repeated subtraction	1
use	a number line to show repeated subtraction	1
	a multiplication table to divide	1
make	a chart to show a total, number in each group, and the number of groups	3
answer	how many equal groups of ___ are in ___?	2
illustrate	how many equal groups of 5 are in 35, 55, and 75	3
compare	multiplication and division	2
write	fact families, or facts that are related and use the same numbers	any number
	five measurement division word problems where you know the size of a group and the total number, and you need to find the number of groups in the total *example:* • 35 people, 5 chairs per table, how many tables are needed?	5
	partition division word problems where you know the total number and the number of groups and you need to know the number in each group *example:* • 35 people, 7 tables, how many people sit at each table?	any number
explain	each of the following: • what happens when a number is divided by 1 • what happens when a number is divided by itself • what happens when a number is divided by zero	3
practice	division facts to 12	any number
memorize	division facts to 12	any number
divide	multiples of 10, 100, and 1,000 mentally	3
	the following with and without regrouping: • 2-digit numbers by 1-digit divisor • 3-digit numbers by 1-digit divisor • multi-digit numbers by 1-digit divisor • 2-digit numbers by 2-digit divisor • 3-digit numbers by 2-digit divisor • 3-digit numbers by 3-digit divisor, and more	any number
describe	when to write a zero to hold a place in a quotient	1
discover	division patterns	1
estimate	quotients of four problems and check	4
use	divisibility rules for 2, 5, and 10	3
outline	a computation strategy that works for you	1
determine	the reasonableness of two quotients	2

Division: Properties and Strategies

Skill	Activity Suggestion	Foldable Parts
K-LK-L	about division properties	3
summarize	the Zero Property of Division	1
draw	a Venn diagram to show what 35 divided by 5 and 35 divided by 7 have in common	3
find	the following: • 24 divided by 6 using related multiplication facts • 24 divided by 6 using division facts • 24 divided by 6 using repeated subtraction • 24 divided by 6 by skip-counting backwards	4

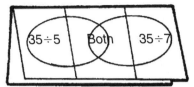

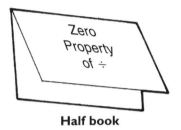

Three-tab Venn diagram

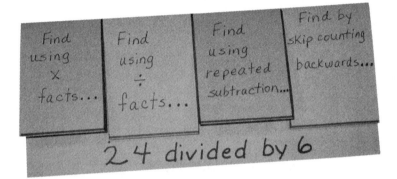

Half book

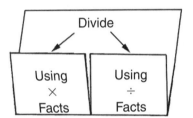

Two-tab concept map

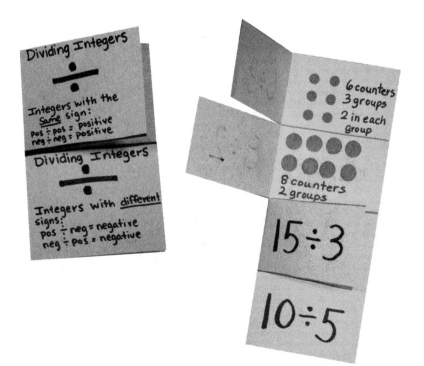

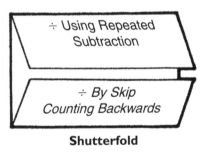

Shutterfold

Integers

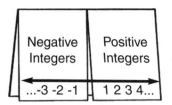

Negative Integers | **Positive Integers**

...-3 -2 -1 | 1 2 3 4...

Two-tab book

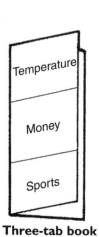

#	Absolute Value

1x2 Chart

Temperature

Money

Sports

Three-tab book

Subtract

Integers with Same Signs | Integers with Different Signs

Concept Map Book

Skill	Activity Suggestion	Foldable Parts
K-LK-L	about integers	3
define	integers and give five examples (...-3, -2, -1, 0, 1, 2, 3, ...)	5
differentiate	between positive and negative numbers	2
make	a number line that includes 6 examples of integers	6
list	examples of positive and negative integers	2
explain	why 0 is neither positive nor negative, but part of the set of integers	1
note	three examples of the use of negative numbers in the real world: temperature, reporting weight loss, distance lost in a game or sport, loss of money, others	3
describe	absolute value as the number of units a number is from 0 on a number line	1
find	the absolute value of 4 numbers	4
graph	given integers on a number line	any number
write	three inequalities using integers	3
add	the following: • integers with the same sign • integers with different, or opposite, signs	any number
subtract	the following: • integers with the same sign • integers with different, or opposite, signs	any number
use	a number line to add and subtract integers	1
multiply	the following: • integers with the same sign • integers with different signs	2
divide	the following: • integers with the same sign • integers with different signs	2
use	a number line to multiply and divide integers	any number

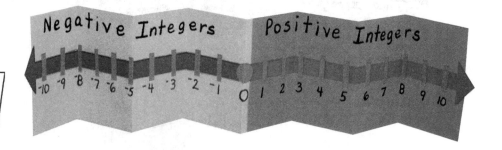

Rational Numbers: General

Skill	Activity Suggestion	Foldable Parts
K-LK-L	about rational numbers	3
define	rational numbers as numbers that can be written as a ratio, or fraction where *a* and *b* are integers and *b* is not equal to 0	1
explain	why whole numbers, integers, fractions, mixed numbers, and decimals are rational numbers	5
prove	every whole number is a rational number, but not every rational number is a whole number	2
list	four rational numbers encountered in a day	4
write	three inequalities involving rational numbers	3
	four negative exponents	4
	five numbers in scientific notation	5
add	rational numbers	any number
subtract	rational numbers	any number
multiply	rational numbers	any number
divide	rational numbers	any number

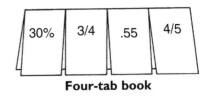

Four-tab book

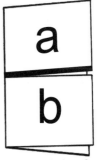

Two-tab book

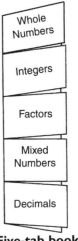

Five-tab book

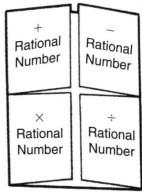

Four-door book

Rational Numbers I Found Today

Student	M	T	W	Th	F
Becky	50% off sale				
Cecile					
Jan		½ price doughnuts			
Ron					
Dale					
Jill					
Sam			25 piece set		
Letty					
Cathy					
Jerry		Vitamin A 100%			
Etta					
Jose					
Cindy					
Bea					

Rational Numbers: Fractions

Two-tab book

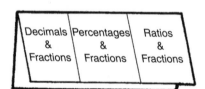

1x2 Chart

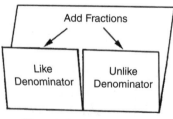

Three-tab book

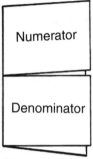

Two-tab concept map

Skill	Activity Suggestion	Foldable Parts
K-LK-L	about fractions	3
define	*fractions* as numbers that name part of a whole	1
label	the *numerator*, *bar*, and *denominator* of a fraction	3
describe	• what the numerator tells • what the denominator tells	2
write	10 whole numbers as fractions	10
find	equivalent fractions, or different fractions that name the same amount, for four given numbers	4
list	at least five equivalent factions for 1/2	5
make	a table to show equivalent fractions for the following: 1/2, 1/3, 1/4, and 3/4	4
use	models to illustrate equivalent fractions	any number
	a number line to order 6 fractions	6
order	four given fractions from smallest to largest	4
	four given fractions from largest to smallest	4
sequence	8 fractions on a number line	8
simplify	10 fractions to their simplest form	10
explain	how you can tell if a fraction can be simplified	1
determine	if 5 given fractions can be reduced further	5
compare	fractions	any number
find	fractions of whole numbers: what is 1/4 of 20	any number
add and subtract	the following: • fractions with like denominators • fractions with unlike denominators • fractions and mixed numbers with like and unlike denominators	any number
multiply	whole numbers by fractions	any number
	fractions by fractions with like and unlike denominators	2
divide	fractions with like and unlike denominators	2
compare	fractions to decimals, percentages, and ratios	3
check	the solutions to addition, subtraction, multiplication, and division of fractions for reasonableness	4
estimate	solutions to addition, subtraction, multiplication, and division of fractions	4
prove	that addition and multiplication of fractional numbers are commutative	2
	that addition and multiplication of fractional numbers are associative	2
	zero is the identity element for addition and one is the identity element for multiplication	2
	the numerator and denominator of a fraction may be multiplied by or divided by the same number without changing the value of the fraction	2
show	each of the following: • fractions are used to name equal parts of a whole • fractions are used to name parts of a set • fractions are used to name a ratio • fractions are used to indicate division	4
understand	that there is in infinite set of fractions, because for every fraction there is always one larger or smaller	1

Mixed Numbers

Skill	Activity Suggestion	Foldable Parts
K-LK-L	about mixed numbers	3
define	a *mixed number* as the sum of a whole number and a fraction	1
list	10 examples of mixed numbers	10
read	four mixed numbers	4
write	six mixed numbers	6
differentiate	between proper and improper fractions	2
write	the following: • mixed numbers as improper fractions • improper fractions as mixed numbers	2
show	three mixed numbers on a number line	3
compare and order	mixed numbers and fractions	2
explain	the following: • how to add mixed numbers in your own words • how to subtract mixed numbers in your own words • how to multiply mixed numbers in your own words • how to multiply a mixed number by a whole number • how to multiply a mixed number by a fraction	any number
estimate	2 sums of mixed numbers	2
	2 products of mixed numbers	2
add and subtract	two mixed numbers and a mixed number and a fraction	2
multiply	the following: • a mixed number by a fraction • a mixed number by a whole number • a mixed number by another mixed number	any number

Three-tab book

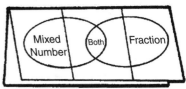

Three-tab Venn diagram

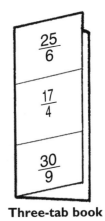

Three-tab book

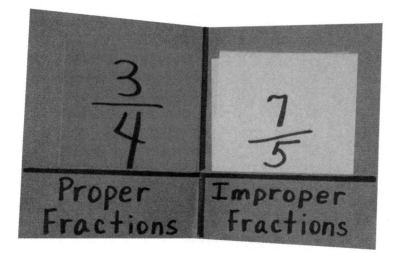

Rational Numbers: Decimals

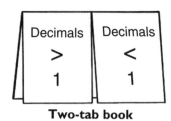

Two-tab book

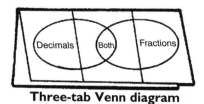

Three-tab Venn diagram

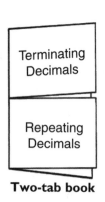

Two-tab book

Skill	Activity Suggestion	Foldable Parts
K-LK-L	about decimals	3
define	a *decimal* as a number that uses a *decimal point* to show place value	1
write and label	a decimal using a decimal point to separate the ones and tenths	2
prove	any number in our numerical system is a decimal because our system has a base-ten foundation	1
read	a decimal correctly: tenths, hundredths, thousandths, ten-thousandths, others	any number
write	6 decimals greater than one	6
make	a decimal number line	1
	a model to illustrate a decimal	1
use	a decimal number line to compare four decimals	4
	a Venn diagram to compare mixed numbers, fractions greater than one, and both	3
write	mixed numbers for a four decimals greater than one	4
	eight equivalent decimals	8
order	6 decimals	6
round	4 decimals	4
add	decimals and decimals	any number
	decimals and whole numbers	any number
subtract	decimals from whole numbers	any number
	decimals from decimals	any number
explain	the importance of aligning decimal points when adding and subtracting in a vertical form	1
multiply and divide	decimals by decimals	any number
	decimals by whole number	any number
explain	in your own words the rule for placement of the decimal point when multiplying decimals	1
	in your own words how to divide by a decimal	1
relate	decimals and fractions	2
	decimals and writing money values	2
	decimals and the measurement of distance, 3.7 miles and 2.5 meters	2
rename	three decimals as fractions	3
	five fractions as decimals	5
find	three equivalent decimals and fractions	3
list	the advantages and disadvantages of using decimals instead of fractions	2
compare	terminating and repeating decimals	2
list	examples of terminating and repeating decimals	2
estimate	the sum of 3 decimals	3
use	decimals to measure distances, report on precipitation amounts, describe sports averages	3

Rational Numbers: Percents

Skill	Activity Suggestion	Foldable Parts
K-LK-L	about percents	3
define	*percent* as a ratio that compares a number to 100 or tells how many out of 100 and give 2 examples *example:* • 7 percent means 7 out of 100 • 24 percent means 24 out of 100	2
explain	the meaning of percent as it relates to hundredths, or per hundred	2
use	the percent symbol when writing percents	1
write	five percents as fractions	5
compare	fractions, decimals, and percents	3
use	fractions, decimals, and percents to name each of 10 numbers	10
find	the percent of 6 given numbers	6
tell	what percent one number is of another	1
relate	percents and circle graphs	2
find	sales tax on 3 items based upon a given % of tax	3
	10% of 50, 500, and 5,000	3
	25% of 10, 100, and 1,000	3
	30% of 100, 200, and 300	3
calculate	discounts based upon percents: 25%, 33%, 40%, 65%	4
make a table	that expresses decimals and fractions as percents	3
	that expresses percents as decimals and fractions	3
collect	four examples of percents from common print: newspaper, magazines, advertisements, others	4
compare and chart	percents that represent numbers equal to one and percents that represent numbers greater than one *examples:* • 100% = 1.00 = 1 • 400% = 4.00 = 4 • 550% = 5.50 = 5 1/2	3

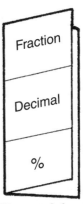

Three-tab book

Fraction	Decimal	%

3x4 Folded chart

%	Fraction

1x2 Chart

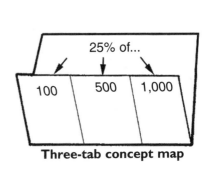

Three-tab concept map

Geometry: Points, Lines, Angles

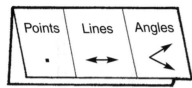

Three-tab book

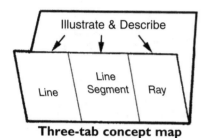

Three-tab concept map

Skill	Activity Suggestion	Foldable Parts
K-LK-L	about points, lines, angles	3
describe	*space* as the set of all points	1
	a *plane* and the infinite number of lines that make up the infinite number of planes in space	1
describe and draw	*points*, *lines*, and *angles*	3
draw and label	the following: • lines and line segments • end points • parallel lines • perpendicular lines • intersecting lines • rays • angles	7
identify	how many end points each of the following have: a line, line segment, and a ray	3
find	the distance between two points on a number line and/or two points in a coordinate plane	2
graph	four ordered pairs on a coordinate plane	4
list	two ways a line can be named	2
draw	and name three line segments	3
	examples of lines that do and do not intersect	2
	parallel lines and perpendicular lines	2
	lines that intersect other lines at a right angle	any number
explain	how a ray is named and draw an example	2
	how two rays form an angle	1
	how the union of two opposite rays form a line	2
label	the parts of an angle: *vertex* and *sides*	2
use	a protractor to measure 4 angles	4
estimate	the measurement of 3 angles and check your estimate	3
classify	angles as right angles, angles greater than a right angle, and angles less than a right angle	3
	angles as acute, right, obtuse, or straight	4
research	complementary and supplementary angles	2

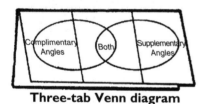

Two-tab book

Three-tab Venn diagram

Three-tab book

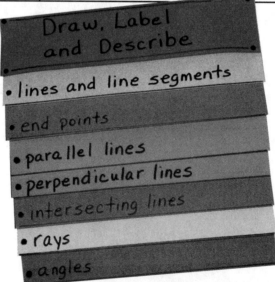

Geometry: 2-Dimensional Figures

Skill	Activity Suggestion	Foldable Parts
K-L‑K‑L	about polygons	3
identify	polygons that are convex and concave	2
describe	*polygons* as closed figures with straight sides in a plane	1
classify	figures as open or closed	2
	polygons by their number of sides	1
draw	examples of open and closed figures	2
read and use	the following prefixes: tri-, quad-, penta-, hexa-, hepta-, octa-, nona-, deca-, dodeca-, n-	10
find	two figures the same size and the same shape	2
identify	the characteristics of a triangle	1
illustrate	six kinds of triangles: equilateral, scalene, isosceles, acute, right, and obtuse	6
sketch	three quadrilaterals, or figures with four sides	3
explain	the six groups of quadrilaterals: • quadrilaterals with no pairs of parallel lines • parallelograms: two pairs of parallel lines • trapezoids: exactly one pair of parallel lines • rectangles: four congruent angles • square: congruent sides and congruent angles • rhombus: parallelogram with congruent sides	6
find	the perimeter of 4 different polygons	4
estimate	the perimeter of 3 polygons and check estimates	3
draw	five polygons on grid paper and count how many squares they cover to determine area	5
find	the area of two polygons	2
describe	and sketch three examples of irregular polygons	3
make a table	to record figures, number of sides/ and corners	3
	to record figures, number of sides/ and angles	3
make	and play with tangrams	1
calculate	the total degree measure of polygons based upon the number of their sides: • 3 sides = 180 degrees • 4 sides = 360 degrees • 5 sides = 540 degrees • 6 sides = 720 degrees	4

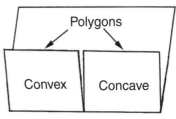

Two-tab concept map

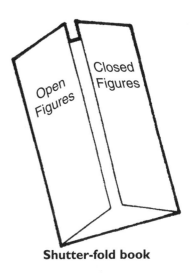

Shutter-fold book

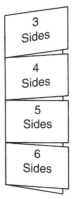

Four-tab book

Six Groups of Quadrilaterals

Quadrilaterals with no pairs of parallel lines

Parallelograms

Trapezoids

Rectangles

Square

Rhombus

Math Words

2-D Figures	# of Sides	# of Angles

3x4 Folded chart

Circles

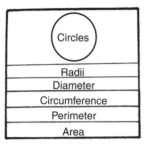

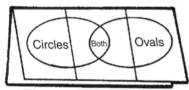

Circles
Radii
Diameter
Circumference
Perimeter
Area

**Layer book
(3 sheets of paper)**

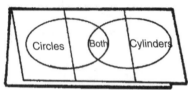

Three-tab Venn diagram

Three-tab Venn diagram

Skill	Activity Suggestion	Foldable Parts
K-LK-L	about circles	3
identify and describe	a *circle* as a special type of a simple closed curve with all points the same distance from a given point	1
draw and label	a circle and the following parts: • center • radius and radii • diameter • circumference • chord • arc	6
explain	how and why circles are divided into 360 degrees	2
use	a compass to draw three circles of varying sizes	3
	a compass to draw three circles of varying sizes on grid paper and estimate their areas by counting grids	3
find	the following: • the perimeter of a circle • the diameter of a circle • the circumference of a circle • the radii of a circle • the area of a given circle	any number
differentiate	between circles and ovals	2
research	the history of and use of pi, or 3.14159....	2
color	the interior of a simple closed curve, or a circle, and the exterior of the same circle	2
cut out	a series of five concentric circles	5
Venn diagram	a circle, a cylinder, both	3

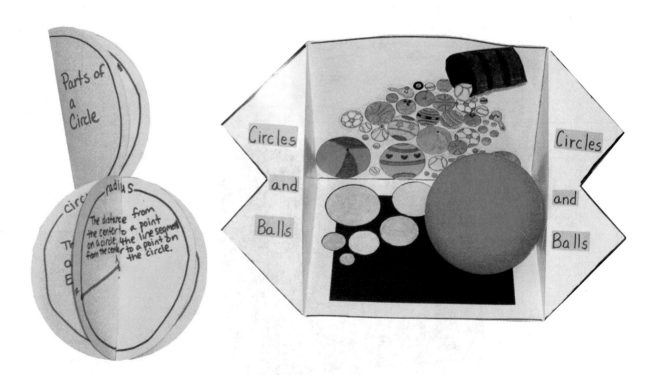

Spatial Relationships

Skill	Activity Suggestion	Foldable Parts
K-LK-L	about spatial relationships	3
identify	*congruent shapes* as shapes the same size and shape and find three examples of congruent shapes	3
	similar shapes as shapes that are the same, but possibly a different size and find three examples of similar shapes	3
	symmetrical shapes and find three symmetrical shapes	3
describe	similar and congruent shapes	2
	rotational symmetry	1
draw	congruent and similar figures	2
	three common symmetrical shapes	3
fold	two figures along a line of symmetry	2
find	figures with no line of symmetry, with one line of symmetry, with two lines of symmetry	3
cut	two symmetrical shapes	2
explain	why all rectangles have rotational symmetry	1
move	triangles by sliding, flipping, and turning	3
demonstrate	translation, reflection, rotation, and tessellations	4

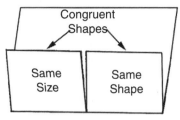

Two-tab concept map

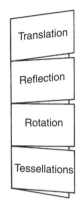

Four-tab book

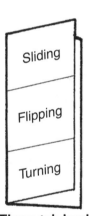

Three-tab book

**Layer book
(2 sheets of paper)**

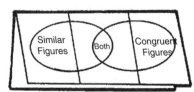

Three-tab Venn diagram

Geometry: 3-Dimensional Figures

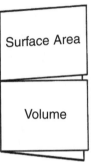

3-D Figures
Cube
Sphere
Pyramid
Cone
Cylinder
Rectangular Prism
Prism

**Layered book
(4 sheets of paper)**

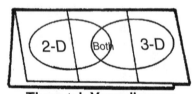

Surface Area
Volume

Two-tab book

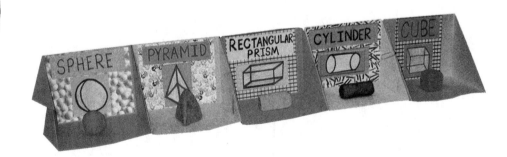

| 2-D | Both | 3-D |

Three-tab Venn diagram

Skill	Activity Suggestion	Foldable Parts
K-LK-L	about 3-dimensional figures	3
define and diagram	*base*, *vertex*, *face*, *edge*, and *net*	5
describe	3-dimensional figures in space	1
draw and label	3-dimensional figures: • rectangular prism • cube • sphere • pyramid • cone • cylinder • prisms	7
sort and classify	3-dimensional objects	any number
make	a table that illustrates and names 3-dimensional figures, number of edges, number of faces, and number of vertices	4
find	the surface area of four 3-dimensional figures	4
define	*volume* as the space a 3-dimensional figure holds	1
model	volume in cubic units	1
find	the volume of three given figures	3
estimate	the volume of two given figures and check estimation	2
list	ways in which you use surface area and volume in your daily life	2
Venn diagram	2-dimensional figures, 3-dimensional figures, both	3
list	examples of 3-dimensional figures encountered in daily life	any number
explain and demonstrate	the following: • the use of 3-dimensional figures in architecture • the use of 3-dimensional figures in furniture design • the use of 3-dimensional figures as storage containers	3
design	a product based upon 3-dimensional figures	1

Figure	Volume	Surface area
#1		
#2		
#3		

3x4 Folded chart

Coordinate Geometry

Skill	Activity Suggestion	Foldable Parts
K-LK-L	about coordinate geometry	3
draw	the intersection of two number lines at their zero points	2
label and describe	the x-axis and the y-axis	2
explain	how a point can be located using a coordinate system	1
	quadrants	1
plot	6 points and name them	6
find	two grids in the world around you	2
use	ordered pairs to identify and locate 5 points on a grid	5
	coordinate graphs to display given points on a grid	any number
read	points as ordered pairs named x and y	any number
	coordinate graphs	any number
describe	ordered pairs: the x point is the horizontal distance and the y point is the vertical distance	2
	how the equally spaced marks along the side of a graph show scale	1
collect	data that can be displayed in a graph and use the graph to report your findings	2
name	the ordered pairs for given points of a grid	any number
plot	points such as (4, 6) and (6, 4) and explain how they differ	any number
K-LK-L	about functions	3
define	function as a relation in which each element of the domain is paired with exactly one element in the range	1
differentiate	between linear and nonlinear functions	2
graph	a function	1
describe	sequences and functions	2
research	Fibonacci sequence	1

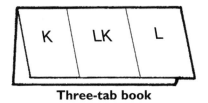

Three-tab book

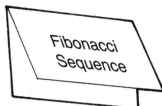

Two-tab book

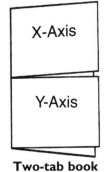

Half book

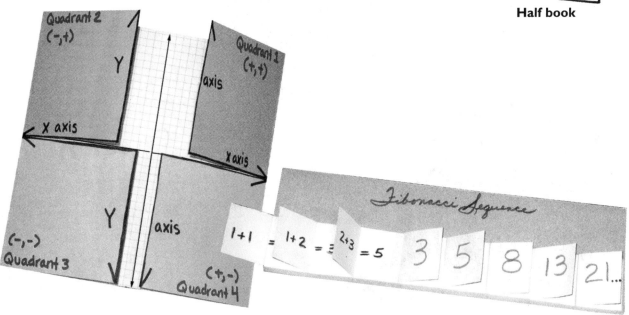

Graphs and Charts

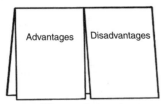

Two-tab book

Graphs

Bar
Line
Circle

**Layer book
(2 sheets of paper)**

Skill	Activity Suggestion	Foldable Parts
K-LK-L	about graphs and charts	3
speculate	as to the history of pictographs	1
list	advantages and disadvantages of using pictographs	2
collect	data from a table to create and write a problem	2
read	the following: • pictographs • bar graphs • line graphs • circle graphs	any number
display	data using the following: • a pictograph and a key • a bar graph • a line graph • a circle graph	any number
explain	how line graphs show data over time, trends, and patterns	3
	how bar graphs compare increases and decreases in quantity over a period of time	2
	how a circle graph shows the parts of something as they relate to the whole	1
compare	line graphs and bar graphs	2
	single and double bar graphs	2

Single Bar Graph   Both   Double Bar Graph

Three-tab Venn diagram

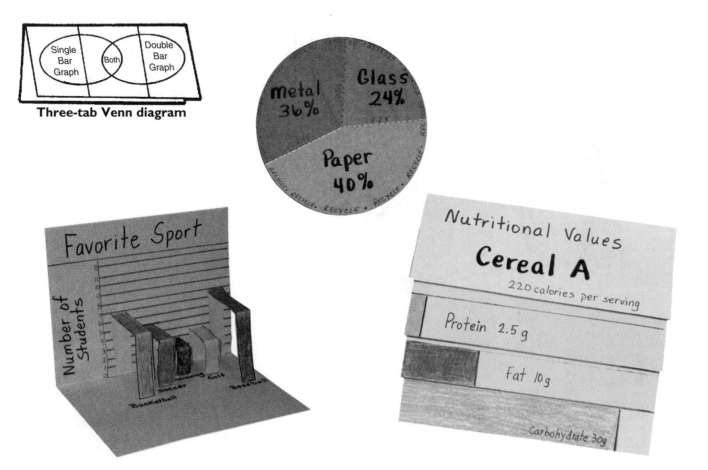

Venn Diagrams

Skill	Activity Suggestion	Foldable Parts
K-LK-L	about diagrams	3
read	Venn diagrams	any number
draw	three Venn diagrams and use them to collect and compare data	3
show	how a Venn diagram can be used to find similarities in data	1
differentiate	between using a two circle Venn diagram and a three circle Venn diagram	2
make	a Venn diagram to display given data and outline the steps you use	2
compare	data presented in a Venn diagram	1
write	four conditional statements in the following format: If ____, then _____.	4
make	a Venn diagram using: • hula hoops • overhead projector transparencies • paper plates	any number

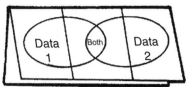

Three-tab Venn diagram

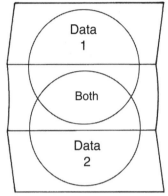

Trifold book

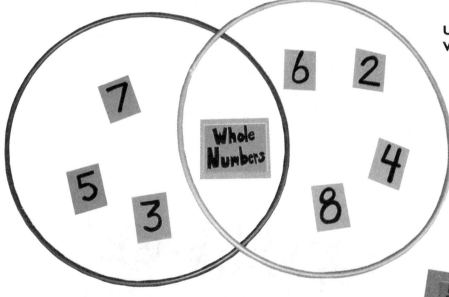

Use hula-hoops to make giant Venn diagrams for the floor

Use paper plates and a brad to make a Venn diagram that can be used with physical objects.

See Dinah Zike's *Great Tables, Graphs, Charts, Diagrams, and Timelines...You Can Make* **pp. 91-96 for other ideas.**

Statistics and Probability

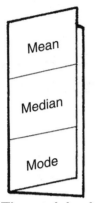

Three-tab book

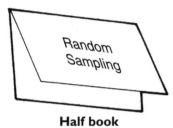

Half book

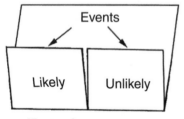

Two-tab concept map

Skill	Activity Suggestion	Foldable Parts
K-LK-L	about statistics and probability	3
define	*statistics* as the mathematics of the collection, organization, and interpretation of numerical data and *probability* as the chance that something will happen	2
describe	events as certain, likely, unlikely, or impossible	4
determine	if events are likely or unlikely	2
define and	*range* and *mode*	2
find	*median*	2
explain	mean, median, and mode	3
	independent and dependent events	2
make	predictions and inferences	any number
find	outcomes	any number
express	the probability of an event	1
use	the term *odds* as a way to describe the chance of an event occurring	1
make	a tally chart and use it to collect data	2
describe	a tally as a way to count by making a mark for each object counted	1
read	a line plot	1
develop	a survey	1
describe and take	a random sampling and report the outcome	2
use	a line plot to organize the results of data collected by a survey	1
	a stem-and-leaf plot	1
	a tree diagram	1
	histograms	1
investigate	experimental probability and report on its use	2
	permutations and combinations	2

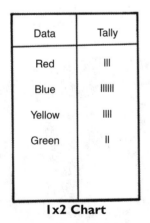

1x2 Chart

Data	Tally
Red	III
Blue	IIIIII
Yellow	IIII
Green	II

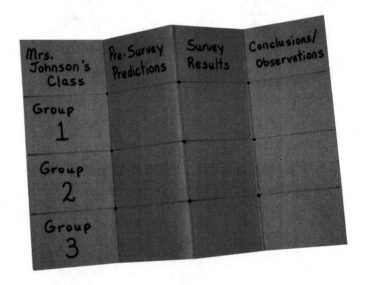

Money

Skill	Activity Suggestion	Foldable Parts
K-LK-L	about money	3
identify	pennies, nickels, dines, quarters, half dollars	5
	one, five, ten, twenty, and hundred dollar bills	5
	the historic figure pictured on each bill	5
make	play money using patterns at the back of this book	1
count	mixed coins to find money amounts	any number
	bills and coins to find money amounts	any number
determine	the fewest number of coins that could be used to make four given money amounts	4
	the fewest number of coins and bills that could be used to make 4 given money amounts	4
read and write	three money amounts using the words "dollars" and "cents"	3
write	four money amounts using numbers and symbols	4
calculate	money amounts	any number
compare	money amounts	any number
make	change by counting up from the cost of an item to the amount paid	1
explain	how to check to make sure the change one is given is correct	1
make	a chart that shows how much something costs, how much was paid, and how much change should be given	3
add	the following: • money amounts with the same coin • money amounts with different coins • money amounts with two coins, three coins, more	any number
subtract	six money amounts	6
estimate	five money amounts	5
round	four money amounts to nearest ten dollars, hundred dollars, thousand dollars, ten-thousand dollars, others	4
compare	money amounts using greater than and less than	2
determine	best buys by comparing money amounts	1
order	six money amounts from least to greatest	6
	six money amounts from greatest to least	6
write	three word problems that include money amounts	3
outline	the steps used to solve each of two money problems	2
use	"per" to mean "for each item"	1
explain	unit price and give two examples	2
determine	the unit price of three objects	3

Five-tab book

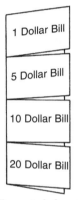

Four-tab book

Coins	Amount

1x2 Chart

Money	Words	Numbers and Symbols
Amount #1		
Amount #2		
Amount #3		

3x4 Folded chart

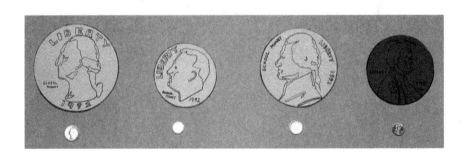

Measurement: Length, Width, Height

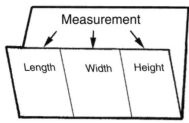

Measurement

Length | Width | Height

Three-tab concept map

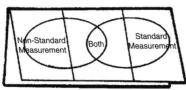

Non-Standard Measurement | Both | Standard Measurement

Three-tab Venn diagram

Measurement	Abbreviation

1x2 Chart

Skill	Activity Suggestion	Foldable Parts
K-LK-L	about the measurement of length, width, height	3
research	the history of the measurement of length, width, and height	3
use	nonstandard units to measure length, width, height	3
name and use	tools for measuring length, width, and height	3
describe	customary units used to measure length: • inch and fractional parts of an inch • inch and foot • foot and yard • inch, foot, and yard	4
write	abbreviations for units of length, width, and height measurement	4
estimate	length, width, or height in customary units	3
measure	length, width, and height in customary units	3
compare	length, width, and height of given objects	3
convert	units of length, width, and height to metric	3
name and use	metric units to measure length: • millimeters (mm) • centimeter (cm) • decimeter (dm) • meter (m)	4
convert	five metric units to customary units	5
make a table	and use it to record the measurement of different objects: object, estimation, measurement	3
list	three or more common uses for length and width	3+

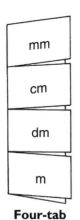

mm

cm

dm

m

Four-tab book

Measurement: Distance

Skill	Activity Suggestion	Foldable Parts
K-LK-L	about the measurement of distance	3
describe	distance as the space between two points and give specific examples	2
research	the history of the measurement of distance	1
use	customary units of measurement for distance: • miles and feet	2
	metric units of measurement for distance: • meters and kilometers	2
write	abbreviations for units of distance measurement	1
estimate	distance using customary units of measurement	1
	distance using metric units of measurement	1
compare	distance in customary units to distance in metric units	2
	the measurement of length and distance	2
measure	distance using customary units	1
	distance using metric units	1
write	two word problems based upon distance	2
investigate	light-years as a measurement of distance and explain how this unit of measurement was developed	2
find	the distance around the Earth's equator and the history of how this measurement was determined	2

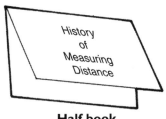

Half book

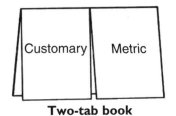

Two-tab book

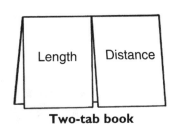

Bound book

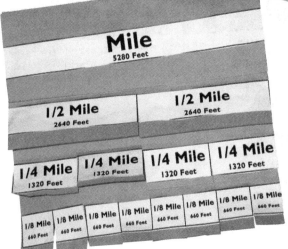

Two-tab book

Measurement: Capacity/Volume

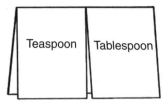

Two-tab book

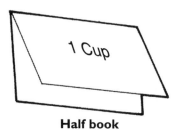

Half book

Volume Customary	Volume Metric

1x2 Chart

Skill	Activity Suggestion	Foldable Parts
K-LK-L	about the measurement of capacity, or volume	3
define	volume as the amount of space something occupies	2
use	common tools to measure capacity	any number
	customary units of measurement and find equivalent measurements: • teaspoon and tablespoon • fluid ounces and cup • cups and pints • cups, pints, and quarts • pints and quarts • quarts and half gallons • pints, quarts, half gallons, and gallons • cups and gallons	2 2 2 3 2 2 4 2
	metric units of measurement: • liter • 1,000 millimeters = 1 liter	2
write	abbreviations for units of capacity measurement	any number
estimate	volume in customary units	any number
	volume in metric units	any number
measure	volume using customary units	any number
	volume using metric units	any number
convert	units of capacity from customary to metric	2
	units of capacity from metric to customary	2
compare	the measurement of volume of a solid and a liquid	2
determine	the number of cubic inches in a cubic foot and the number of cubic centimeters in a cubic meter	2

Measurement: Weight

Skill	Activity Suggestion	Foldable Parts
K-LK-L	about the measurement of weight	3
define	weight as the force of gravity pulling on an object	1
research	the history of the measurement of weight	1
use	tools to measure weight	any number
	customary units of measurement: • ounces and pounds	2
	metric units of measurement: • grams and kilograms	2
write	abbreviations for units of weight measurement • lb. • oz. • dr. • gr. • kg. • g. • cg • mg • mcg	any number
explain	why there are 1,000 grams in a kilogram	1
	how many ounces there are in a pound and half pound	2
estimate	weight in customary and metric units	2
compare	weights in customary and metric units	2
measure	weight in customary and metric units	2
explain	why objects have no weight in space	1
estimate	the weight of four objects based upon personal experiences, and check your estimations by weighing the objects	4

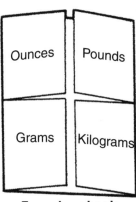

Four-door book

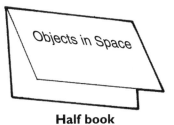

1x2 Chart

Half book

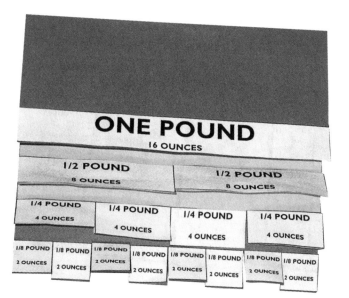

Vocabulary book

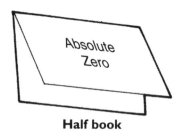

Half book

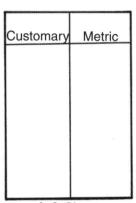

Temperature	9:00 AM.	3:00 PM.
Monday		
Wednesday		
Friday		

3x4 Folded chart

Customary	Metric

1x2 Chart

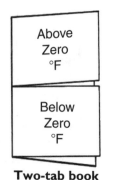

Two-tab book

Measurement: Temperature

Skill	Activity Suggestion	Foldable Parts
K-LK-L	about the measurement of temperature	3
research	the history of the measurement of temperature	1
use	tools to measure temperature	1
	customary units to measure temperature: • Fahrenheit (F) thermometer	1
	metric units to measure temperature: • Celsius (C) thermometer	1
establish	a weather center with tools to measure temperature and document temperature readings over a period of time	any number
write	abbreviations for units of temperature measurement	any number
estimate	temperature in customary and metric units	2
measure	temperature in Fahrenheit and Celsius	2
compare	temperature readings at different times of the day	any number
describe	three instances in which temperature is important	3
convert	six customary units to metric	6
	six metric units to customary	6
explain	temperatures above and below zero in customary and metric measurement	2
research and graph	freezing and boiling points in customary and metric	2
	high and low temperatures around the world	2
	average human body temperature and average body temperatures of three animals	4
	Kelvin, thermodynamic temperature unit	1
	absolute zero, -273.15°C or -495.67°F	2
write	three word problems based upon temperature	3

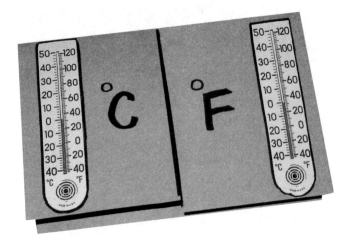

Measurement: Time

Skill	Activity Suggestion	Foldable Parts
K-LK-L	about the measurement of time	3
define	second, minute, hour	3
	quarter-hour and half-hour	2
use	the terms morning, noon, and night to describe time	3
	tools to measure time	any number
	a clock to count by 5's	12
estimate	the passing of time	1
explain	elapsed time, or the time from the beginning of something to the end	1
	why there are 60 minutes in an hour, 30 minutes in a half hour, and 15 minutes in a quarter hour	3
tell	time in the following ways: • time in relation to events • time in hours or to the nearest hour • time in half-hours or to the nearest half-hour • time to the nearest 5 minutes • time before and after the hour	any number
show	the following: • how many quarter hours there are in an hour • that there are 60 seconds in a minute • that there are 60 minutes in an hour • that there are 24 hours in a day	4
read	time using a digit clock and an analog clock	2
order	four given times from most distant to most recent	4
describe	A.M. and P.M.	2
make a chart	that shows how many half hours and quarter hours there are in a given number of hours	2
	that shows how many minutes and seconds there are in a given number of hours	2
	and use it to record the hour and minute at different times of the day	2
	to record elapsed time: beginning time, ending time, and the time elapsed between the two	3
research	the history of the measurement of time	1
explain	the base 60 number system of the Babylonians and give examples of how it is still used today	2
tell	time using the terms "before the hour" and "after the hour"	2

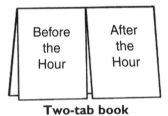

Four-tab book

Two-tab book

Two-tab book

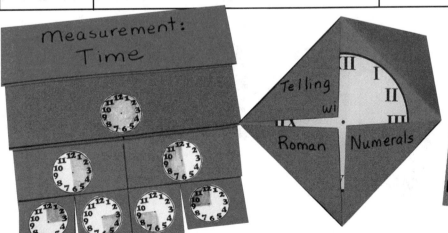

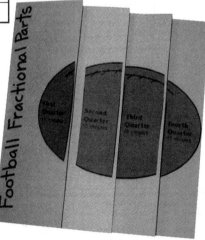

Measurement: Calendars

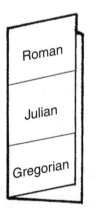

Four-door book

Emperor Constantine | What
When | Where

Skill	Activity Suggestion	Foldable Parts
K-LK-L	about the use of calendars	3
make a time line	on the development of our modern calendar	any number
research	the who, what, when, where of Emperor Constantine, and the establishment of a seven day week with Sunday as the first day	4
memorize	the days of the week and recite them in order	7
	the months of the year and recite them in order	12
calculate	how many hours there are in a day, a week, a specific month, and a year	4 or 5
count	the number of days in a week and a year	2
	how many weeks there are in a year	1
observe	a calendar and note how many days there are in each of the 12 months	12
make	a calendar for the current year	12
use	a calendar to determine how many days it is until a given date? how many weeks?	2
describe	how a calendar can be used to skip count by sevens	1
use	ordinal numbers to find dates on a calendar *example:* • find the date of the third Monday of the month	any number
relate	calendars and time lines	2
research	and report on the history of the calendar	2
list	the different types of information displayed on a calendar: moon phases, holidays, first day of a season, birthdays of historic people, other	any number
research	the origin of the name's of the days of the week	7
	the origin of the name's of the months of the year	12
	the Gregorian calendar and its use	2
compare	the Roman calendar, Julian calendar, and the Gregorian calendar	3
describe	leap year and explain its purpose	2
Venn diagram	a mean solar day (24 hours 3 minutes 56.55 seconds), a mean sidereal time (23 hours 56 minutes 4.1 seconds) and both	3
compare	the use of the moon to tell time and the use of the sun to tell time	2

Days of the Week
Sunday
Monday
Tuesday
Wednesday
Thursday
Friday
Saturday

Layered book
(4 sheets of paper)

Roman

Julian

Gregorian

Three-tab book

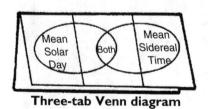

Mean Solar Day | Both | Mean Sidereal Time

Three-tab Venn diagram

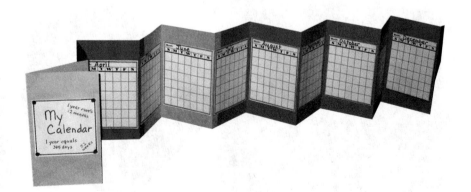

Math
Graphics
and
Activities

Large Half Dollar: Front

Large Quarter: Front

Large Quarter: Back

Large Dime: Front and Back

Large Nickel: Front and Back

Large Penny: Front and Back

One Dollar Bill: Front and Back

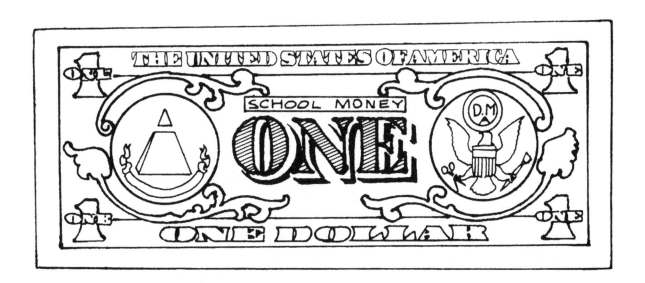

Five Dollar Bill: Front and Back

Ten Dollar Bill: Front and Back

Twenty Dollar Bill: Front and Back

Small Money Pieces: Mixed

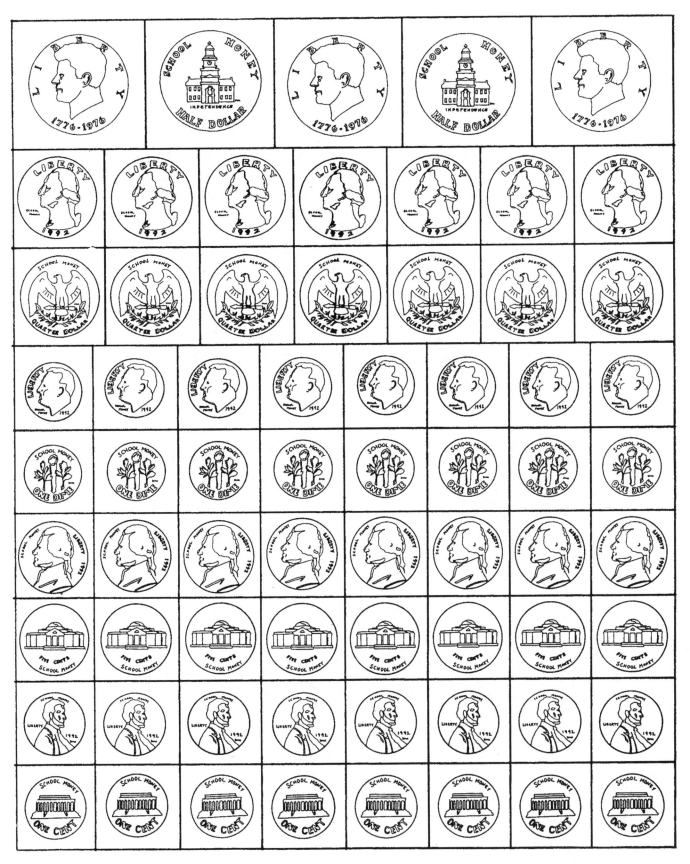

Money Equivalencies:

Use With Layered-Look Book

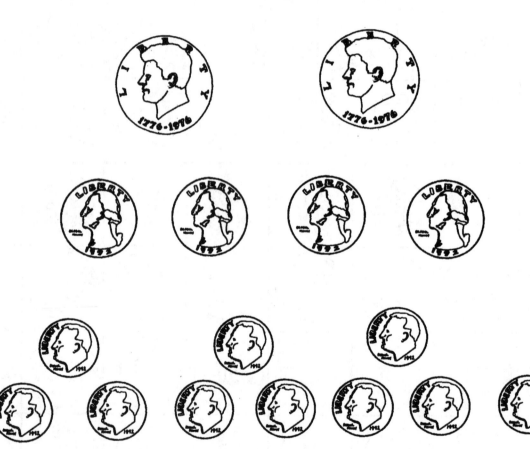

Money Match Book

Glue different combinations of coins inside this money chest and calculate how much money is inside.

Time Match Book:

Draw hands on the clock to illustrate a time. Under the clock tab write what happened at that time.

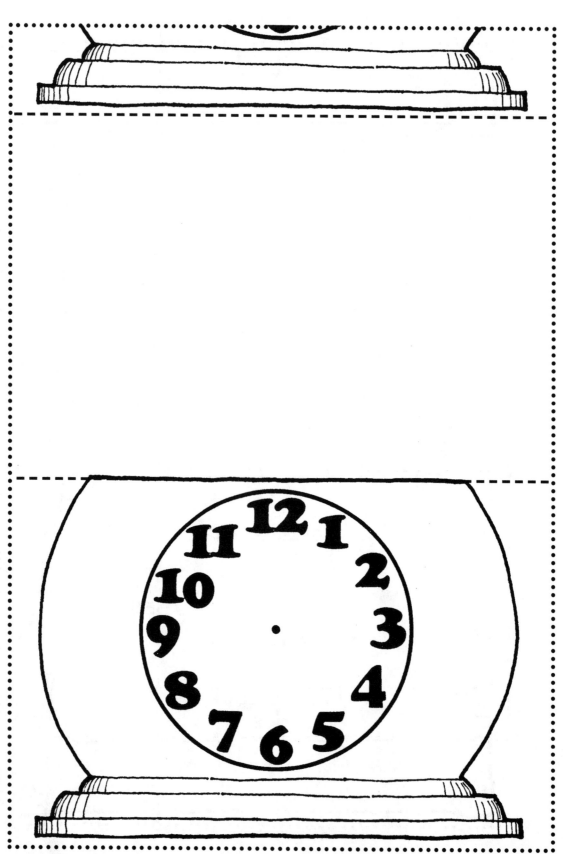

Large Clock Face

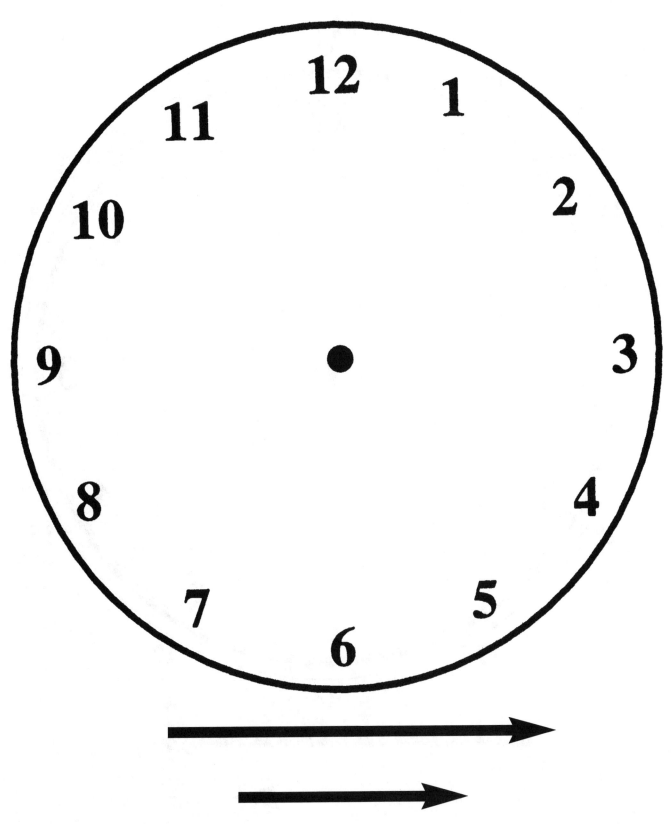

Large Clock Face:
Military Time

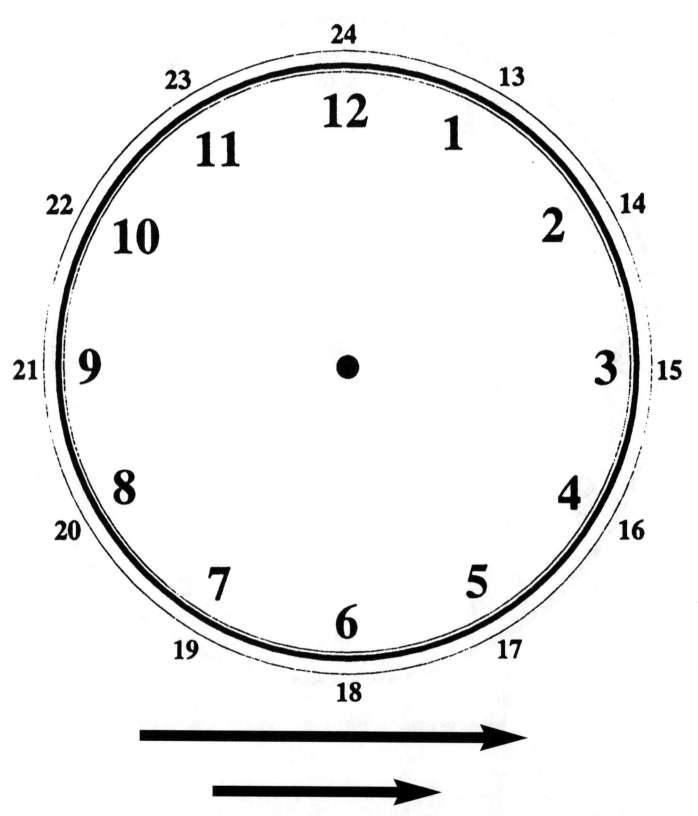

Large Clock Face:
Roman Numerals

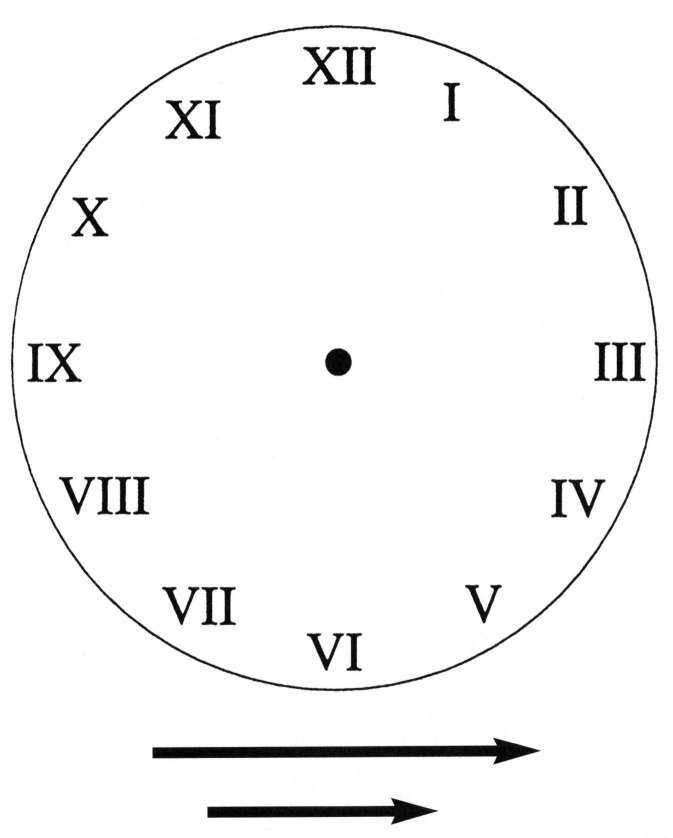

Small Clock Faces

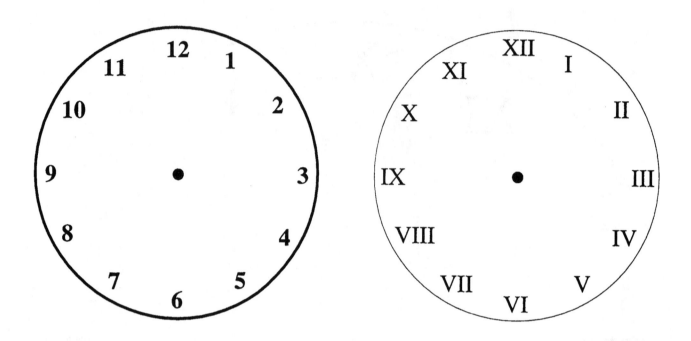

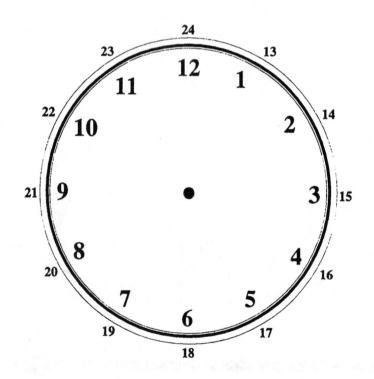

Hour, Minute, and Second:
Use With Three-Tab Book

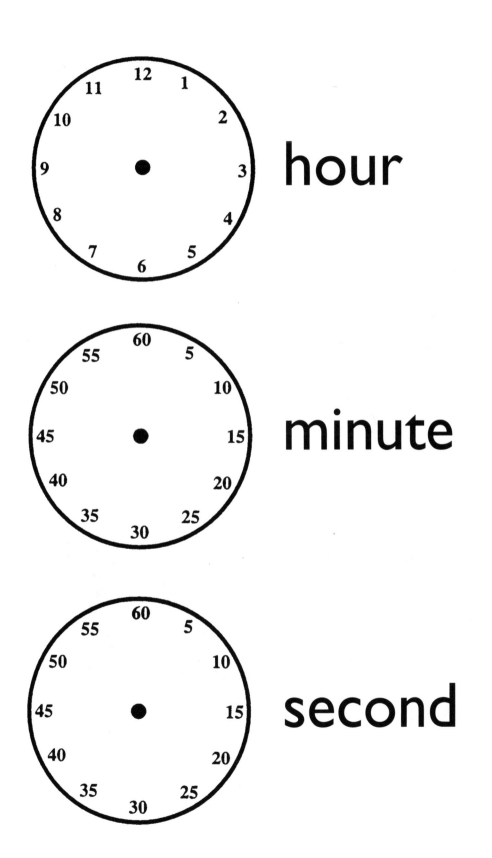

hour

minute

second

Small Clock Faces:

Use With Layered-Look Book

Large Calendar

Month:						
S	**M**	**T**	**W**	**T**	**F**	**S**

Small Calendars

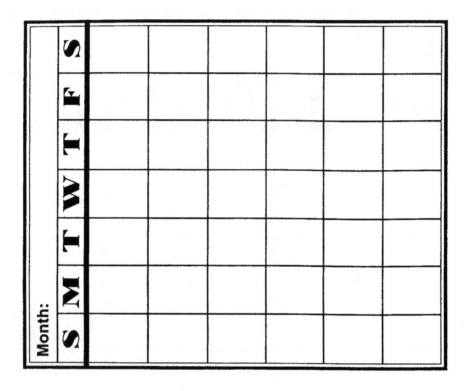

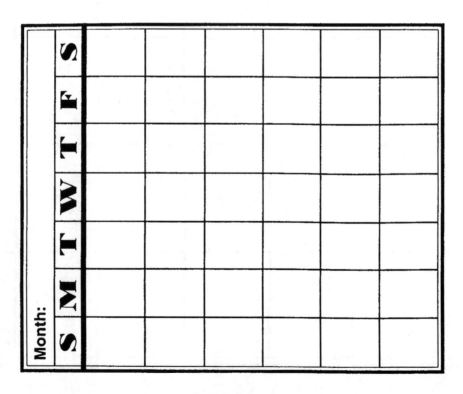

6 Inch Rulers
Use With Layered-Look Book

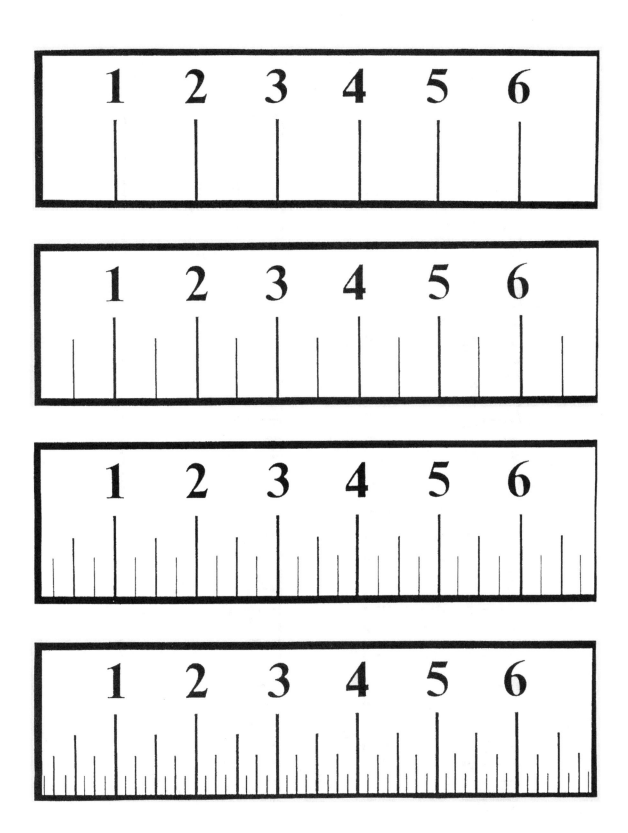

Metric Rulers

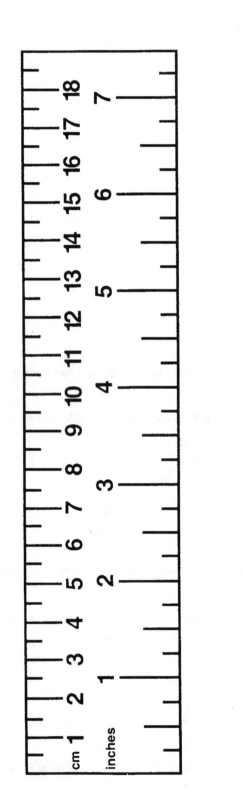

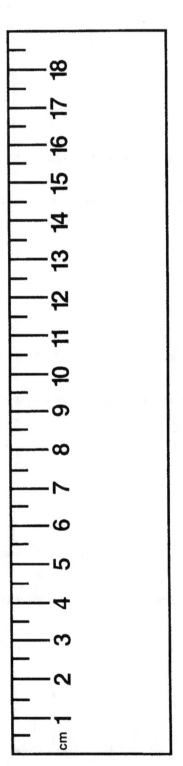

Miles and Feet

Use With Layered-Look Book

Mile	1/2 Mile	1/4 Mile	1/8 Mile
Mile 5280 Feet	**1/2 Mile** 2640 Feet	**1/4 Mile** 1320 Feet	**1/8 Mile** 660 Feet
		1/4 Mile 1320 Feet	**1/8 Mile** 660 Feet
			1/8 Mile 660 Feet
			1/8 Mile 660 Feet
	1/2 Mile 2640 Feet	**1/4 Mile** 1320 Feet	**1/8 Mile** 660 Feet
			1/8 Mile 660 Feet
		1/4 Mile 1320 Feet	**1/8 Mile** 660 Feet
			1/8 Mile 660 Feet

Kilometers and Meters

Use With Layered-Look Book

Kilometers 1000 Meters	1/2 Kilometers 500 Meters	1/4 Km 250 Meters	1/10 Km 100 m
		1/4 Km 250 Meters	1/10 Km 100 m
	1/2 Kilometer 500 Meters	1/4 Km 250 Meters	1/10 Km 100 m
		1/4 Km 250 Meters	1/10 Km 100 m

Liquid Measurement

Use With Layered-Look Book

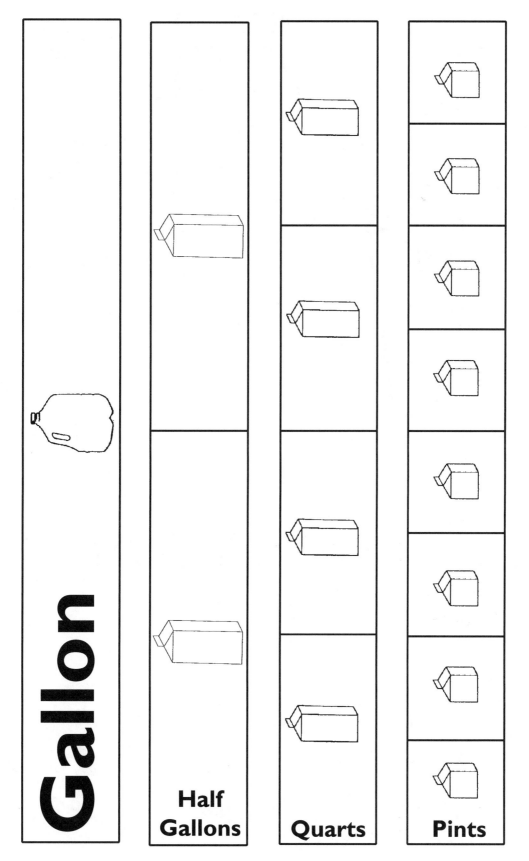

Gallon

Half Gallons

Quarts

Pints

Gallon: Bulletin Board

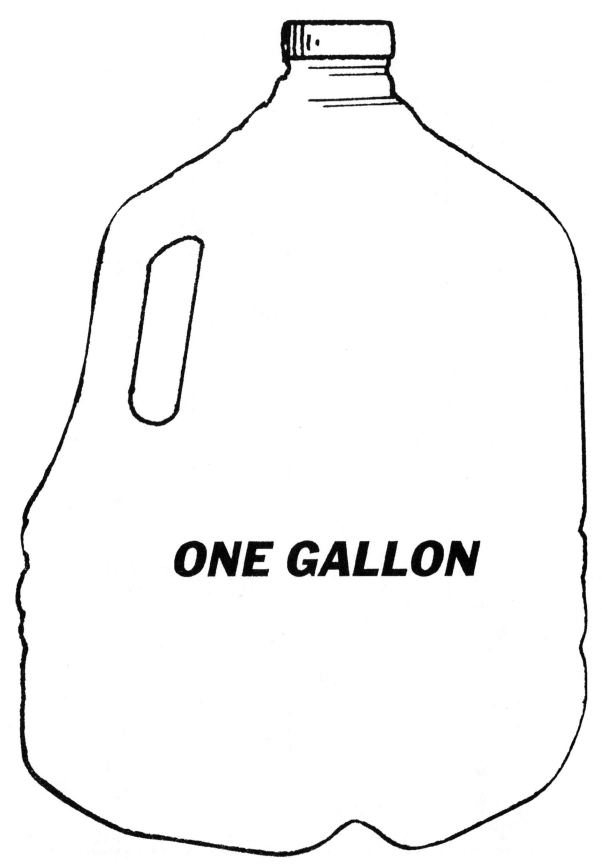

ONE GALLON

Quart: Bulletin Board

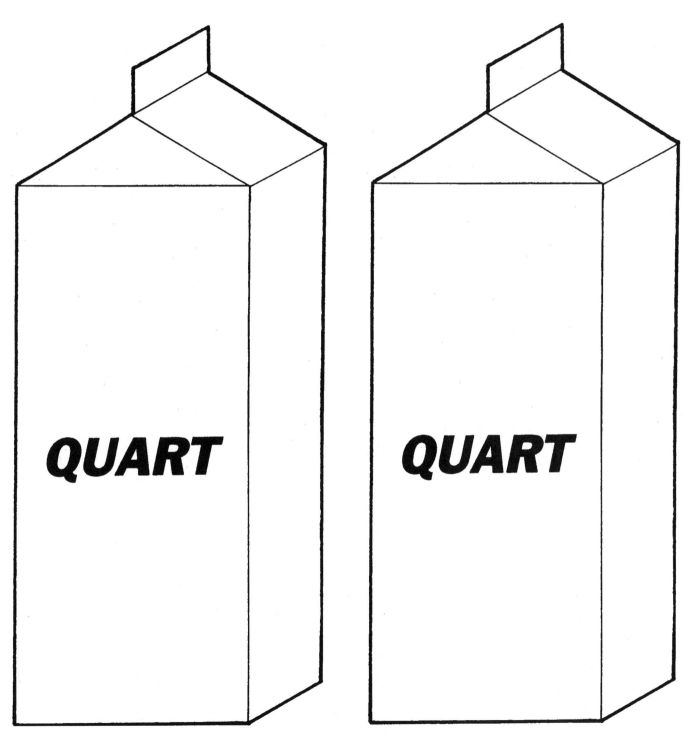

Pint: Bulletin Board

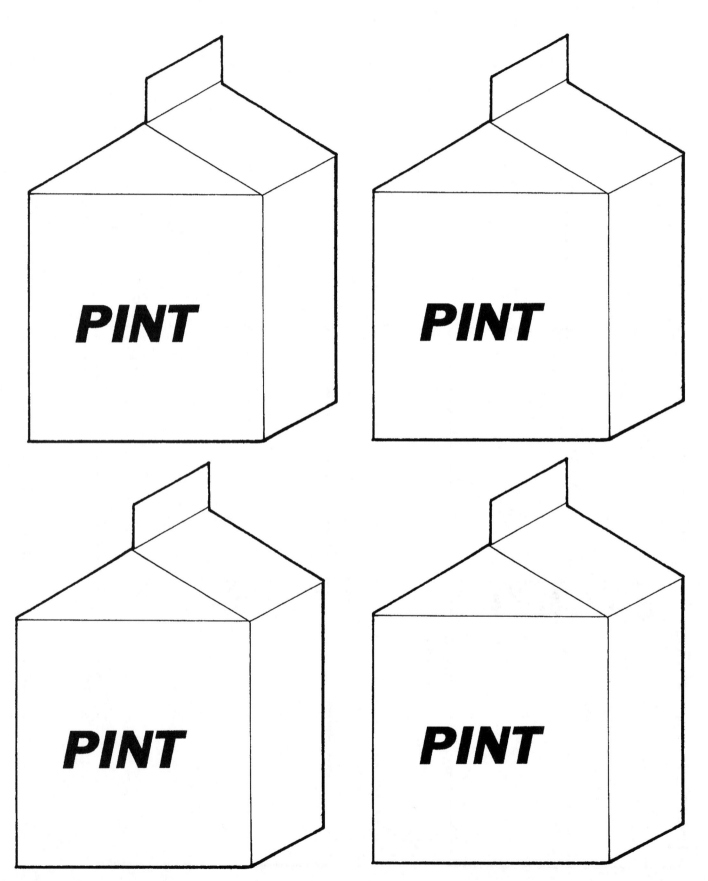

Student Patterns

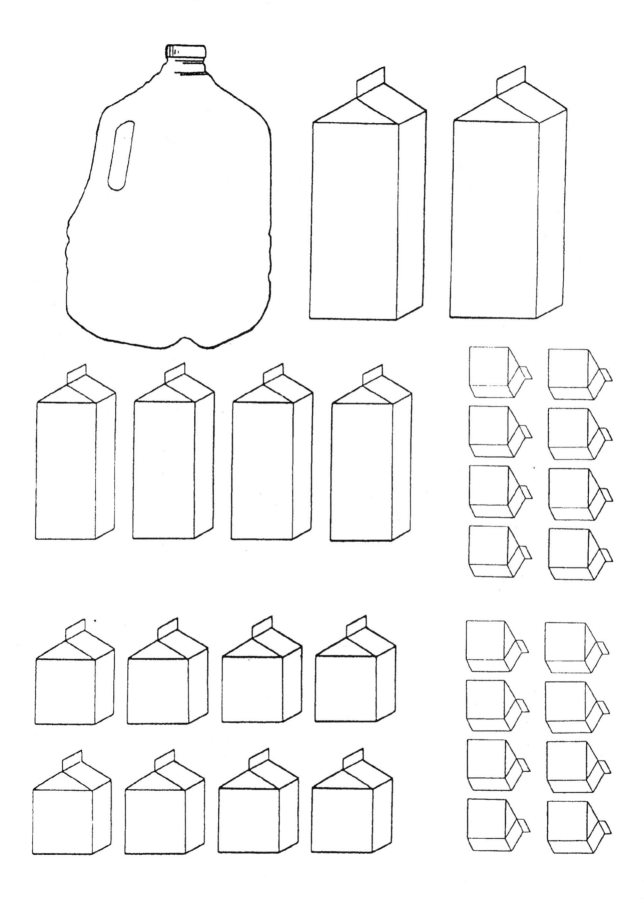

Measuring Cups

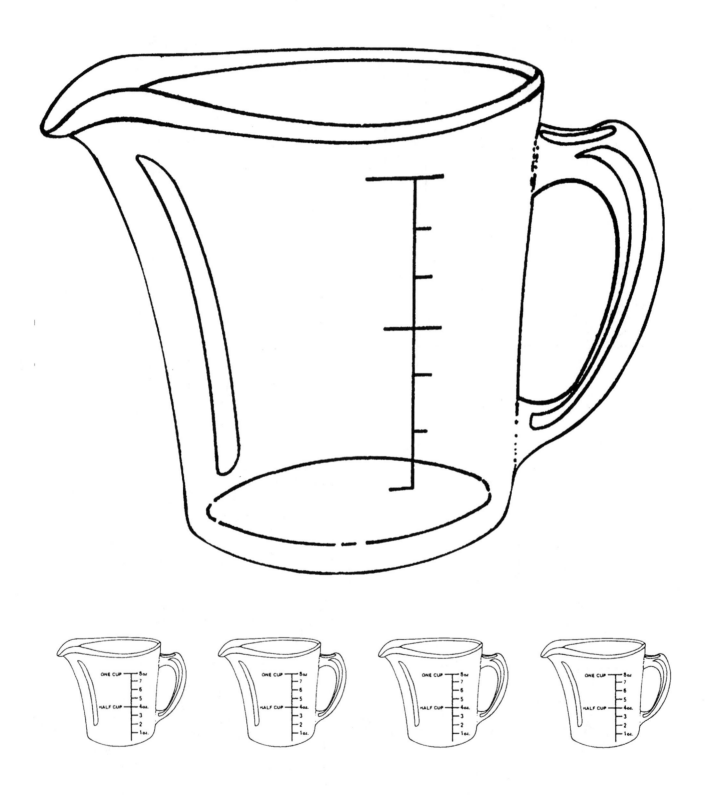

Cups and Ounces
Use With Layered-Look Book

ONE CUP
8 OUNCES

1/2 CUP
4 OUNCES

1/2 CUP
4 OUNCES

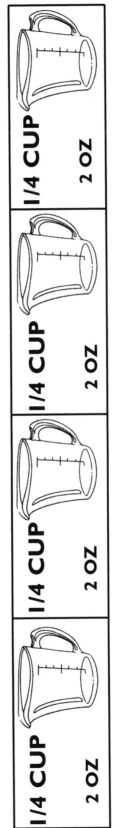

1/4 CUP	1/4 CUP	1/4 CUP	1/4 CUP
2 OZ	2 OZ	2 OZ	2 OZ

1/8 CUP	1/8 CUP	1/8 CUP	1/8 CUP	1/8 CUP	1/8 CUP	1/8 CUP	1/8 CUP
1 OZ	1 OZ	1 OZ	1 OZ	1 OZ	1 OZ	1 OZ	1 OZ

Pounds and Ounces

Use with Layered-Look Book

ONE POUND

16 OUNCES

1/2 POUND

8 OUNCES

1/2 POUND

8 OUNCES

1/4 POUND

4 OUNCES

1/4 POUND

4 OUNCES

1/4 POUND

4 OUNCES

1/4 POUND

4 OUNCES

1/8 POUND	1/8 POUND	1/8 POUND	1/8 POUND	1/8 POUND	1/8 POUND	1/8 POUND	1/8 POUND
2 OUNCES	2 OUNCES	2 OUNCES	2 OUNCES	2 OUNCES	2 OUNCES	2 OUNCES	2 OUNCES

Beakers

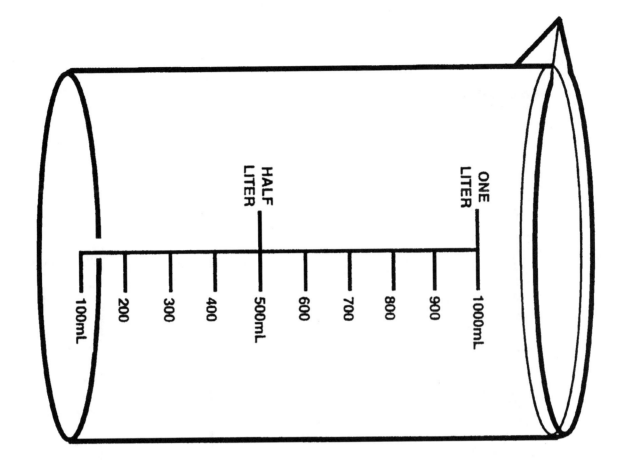

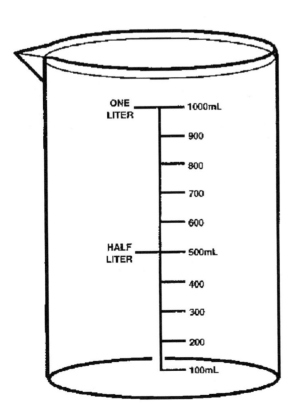

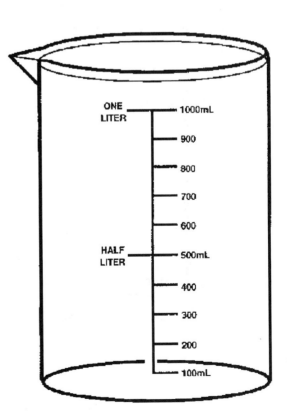

Cylinders

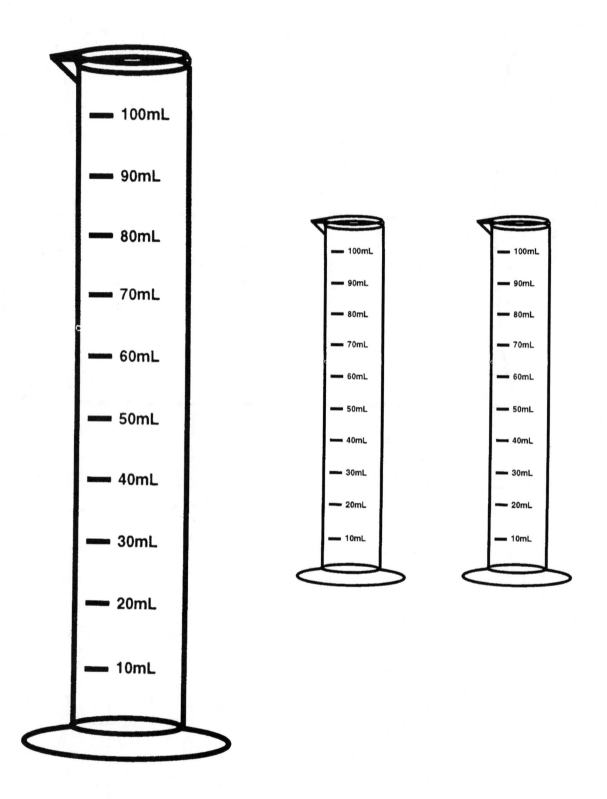

Flasks

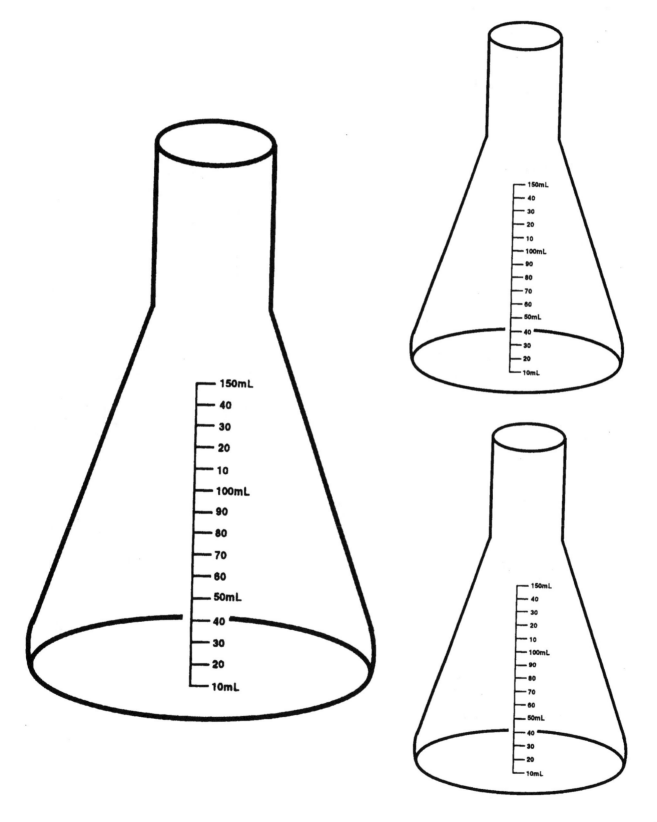

Rain Gauges

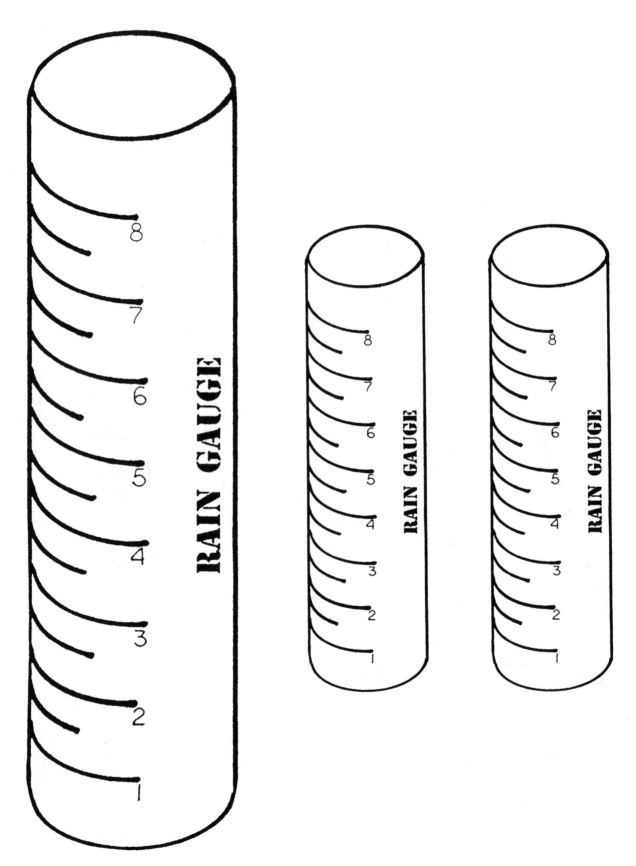

Thermometers

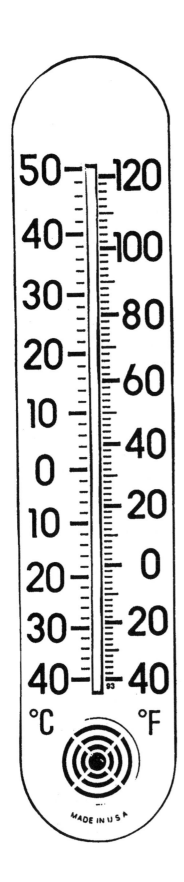

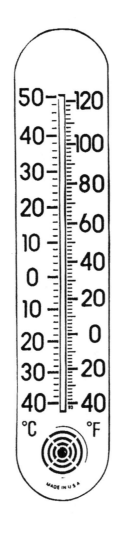

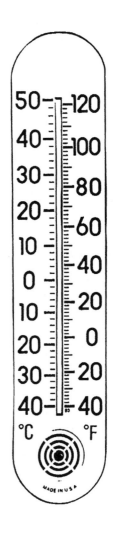

Squares: Fractional Parts

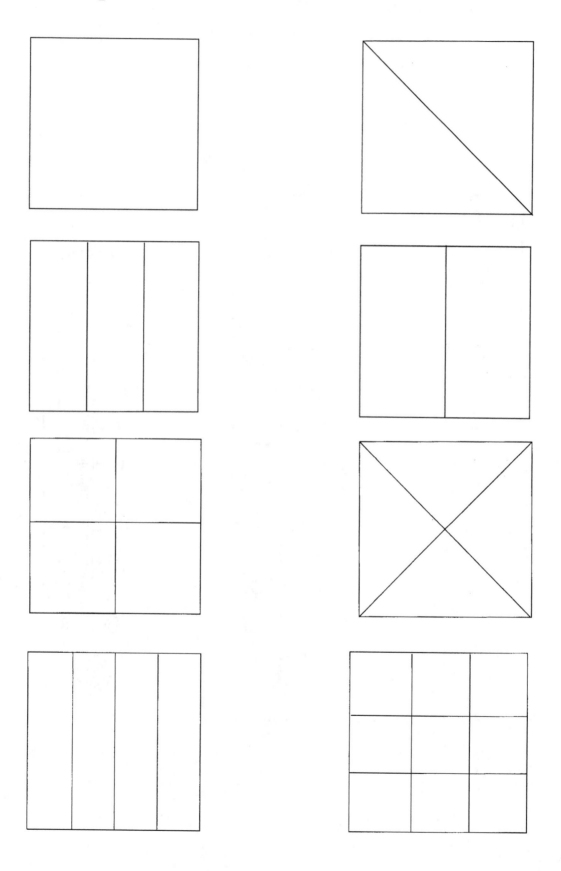

Circles: Fractional Parts

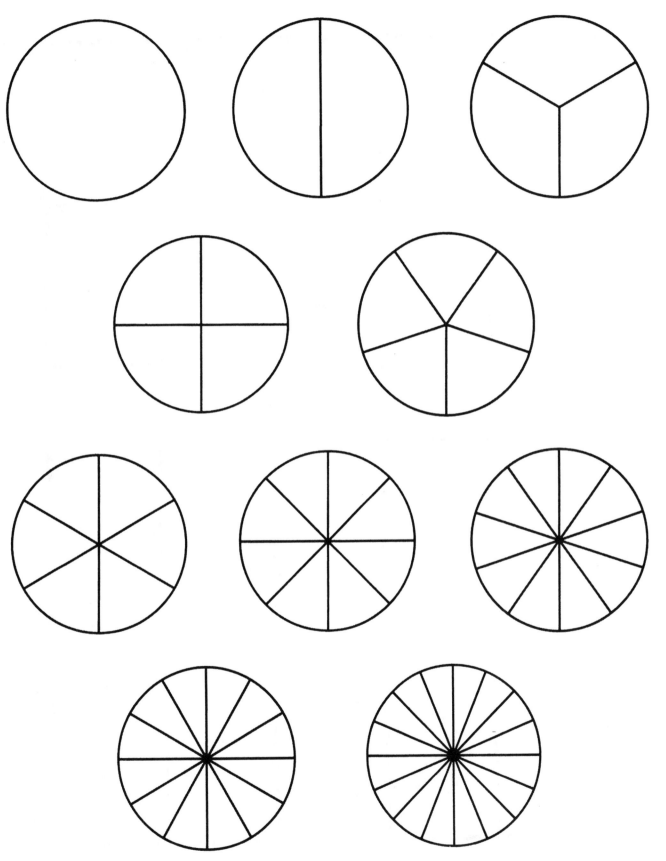

Mix and Match Fraction Bars

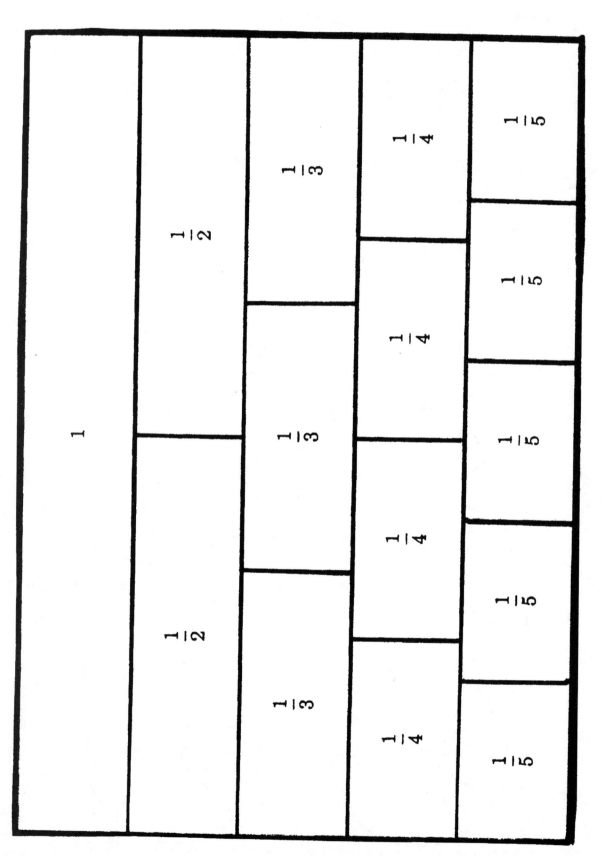

Mix and Match Fraction Bars

$\frac{1}{6}$	$\frac{1}{8}$	$\frac{1}{9}$	$\frac{1}{10}$	$\frac{1}{12}$
				$\frac{1}{12}$
$\frac{1}{6}$	$\frac{1}{8}$	$\frac{1}{9}$	$\frac{1}{10}$	$\frac{1}{12}$
	$\frac{1}{8}$	$\frac{1}{9}$	$\frac{1}{10}$	$\frac{1}{12}$
$\frac{1}{6}$			$\frac{1}{10}$	$\frac{1}{12}$
	$\frac{1}{8}$	$\frac{1}{9}$		
$\frac{1}{6}$		$\frac{1}{9}$	$\frac{1}{10}$	$\frac{1}{12}$
	$\frac{1}{8}$		$\frac{1}{10}$	$\frac{1}{12}$
$\frac{1}{6}$		$\frac{1}{9}$		
	$\frac{1}{8}$		$\frac{1}{10}$	$\frac{1}{12}$
		$\frac{1}{9}$		$\frac{1}{12}$
$\frac{1}{6}$	$\frac{1}{8}$	$\frac{1}{9}$	$\frac{1}{10}$	$\frac{1}{12}$

Fractional Parts: Musical Notes

Use With Layered-Look Book

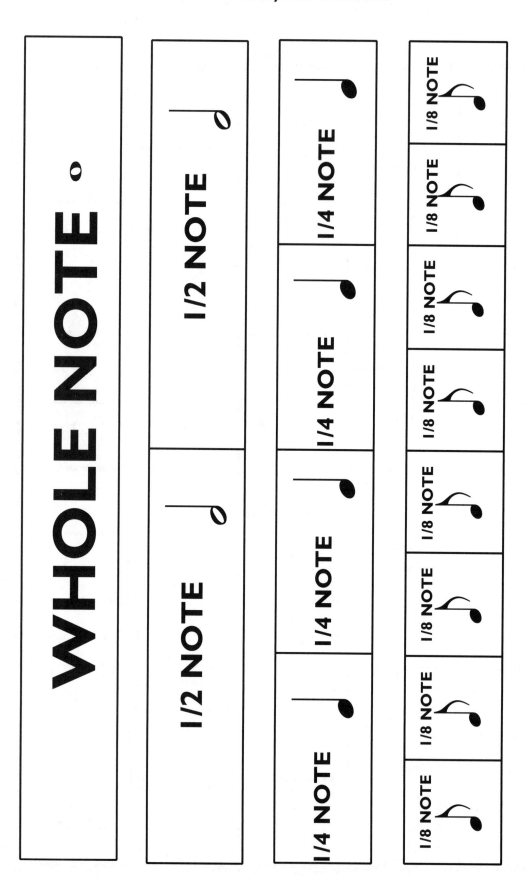

Football Fractional Parts

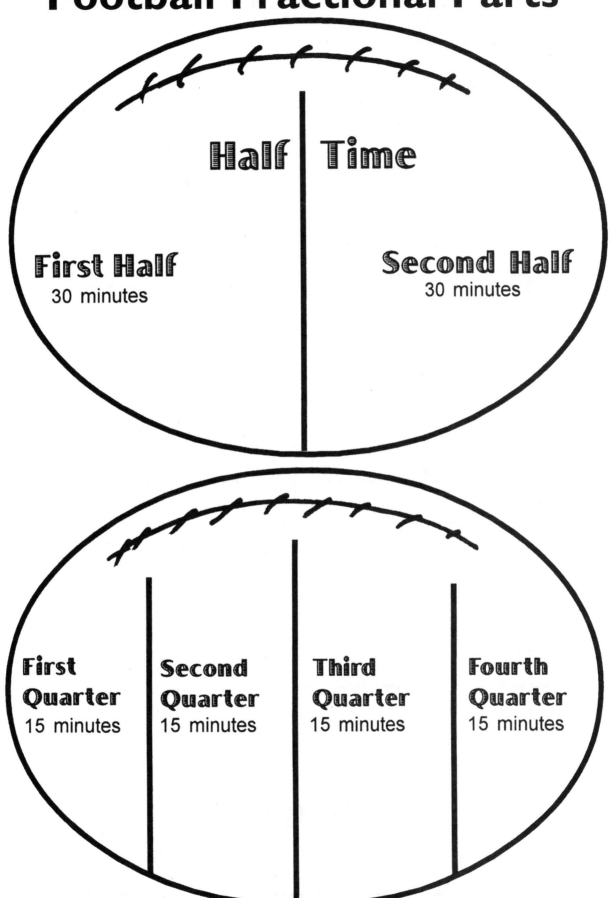

Half Time

First Half
30 minutes

Second Half
30 minutes

First Quarter
15 minutes

Second Quarter
15 minutes

Third Quarter
15 minutes

Fourth Quarter
15 minutes

Two-Dimensional Shapes

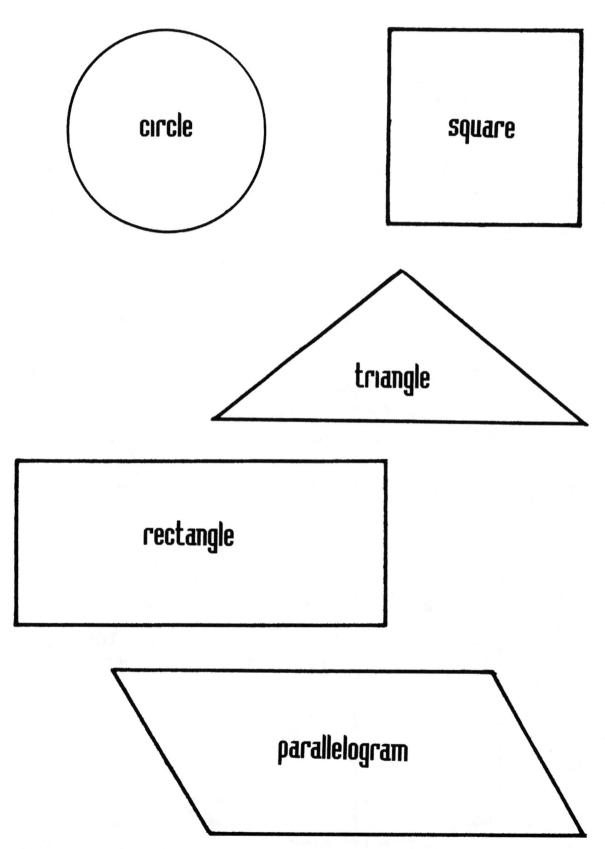

circle

square

triangle

rectangle

parallelogram

Three-Dimensional Shapes

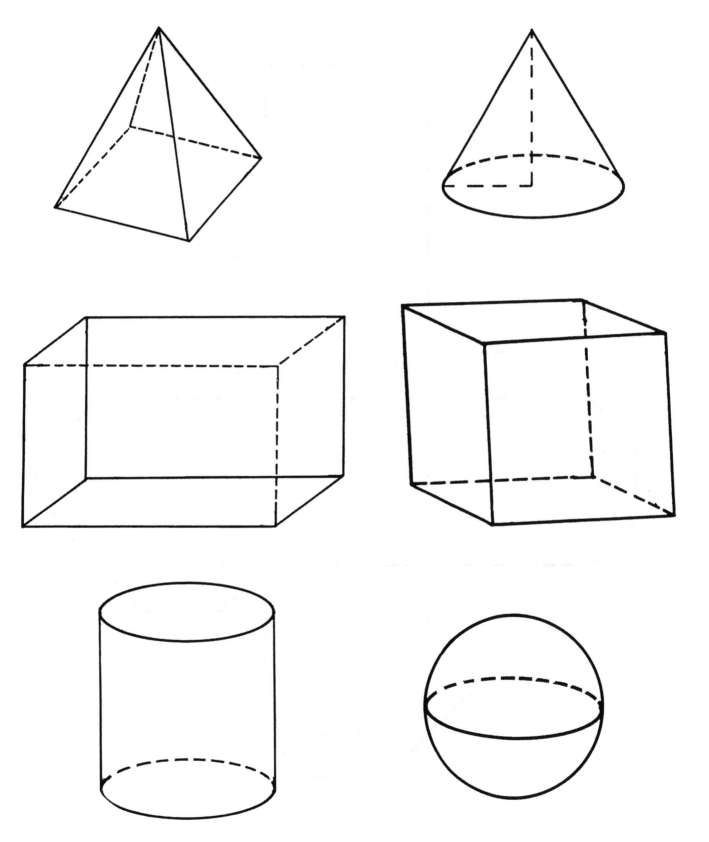

3-D Cube Model

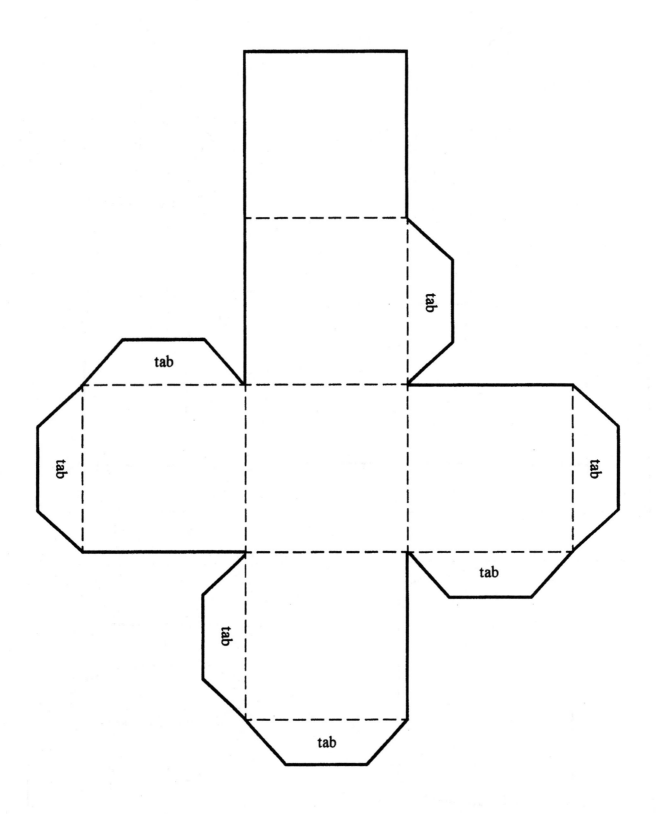

3-D Tetrahedron Model

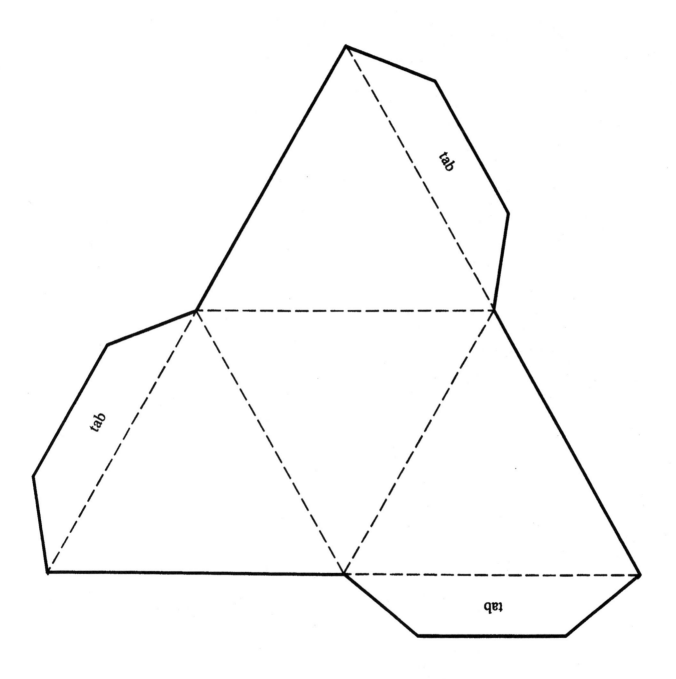

3-D Box Model

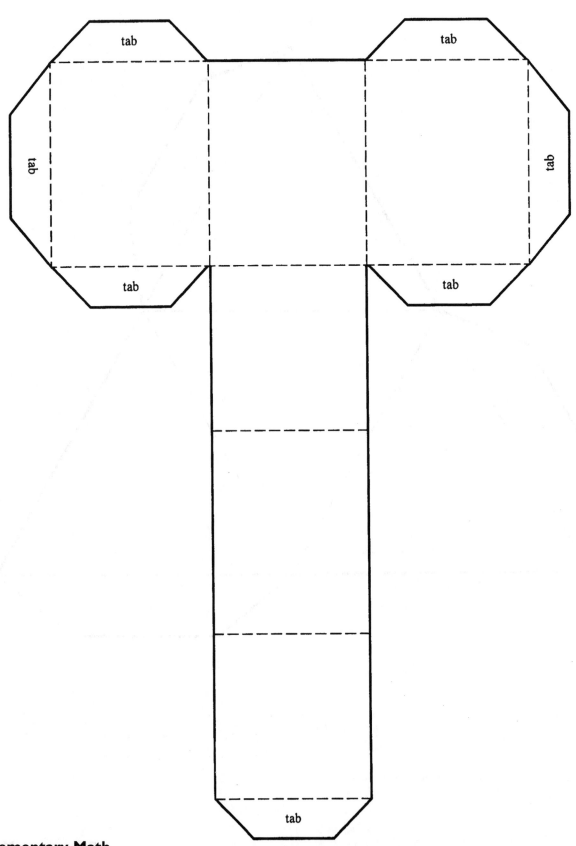

Angles

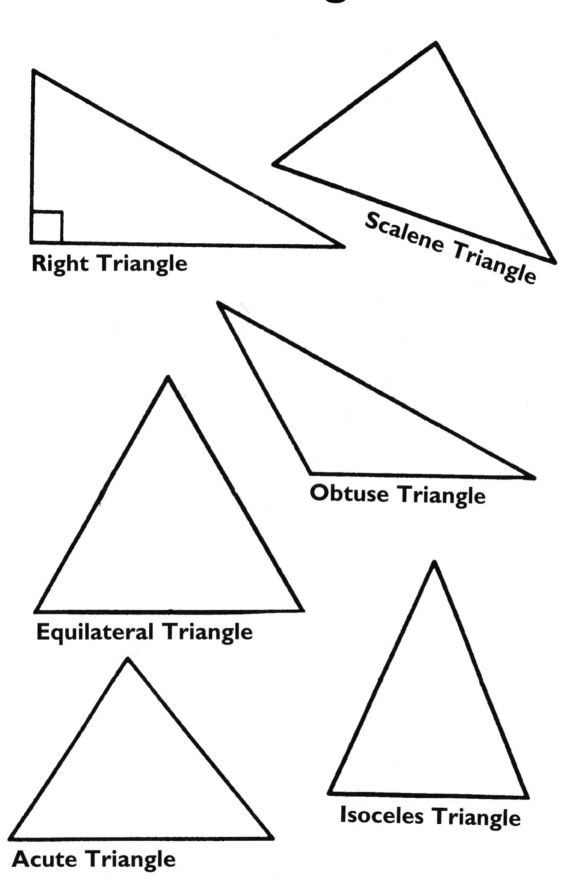

Right Triangle

Scalene Triangle

Obtuse Triangle

Equilateral Triangle

Acute Triangle

Isoceles Triangle

Tangram

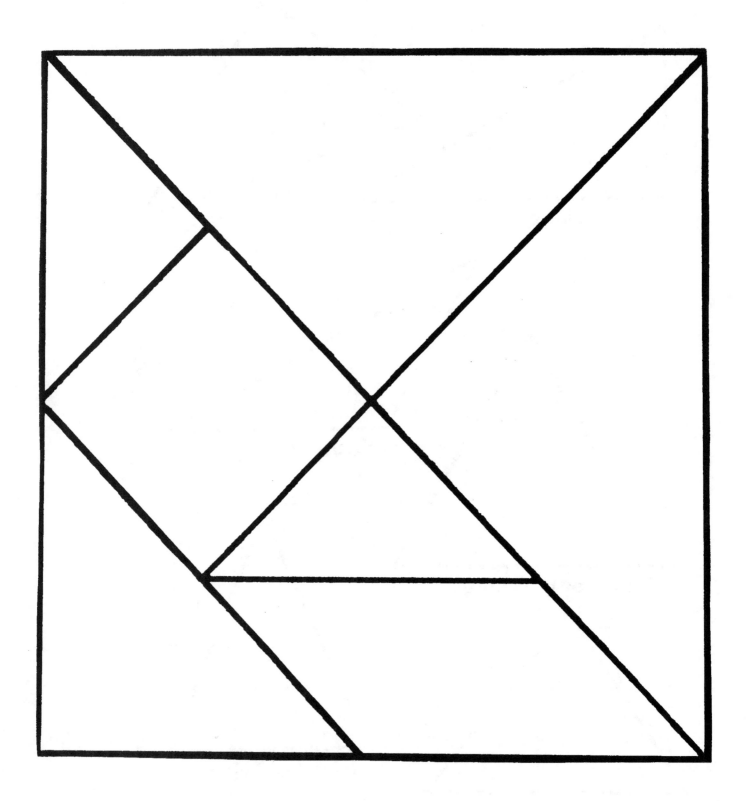

Protractors

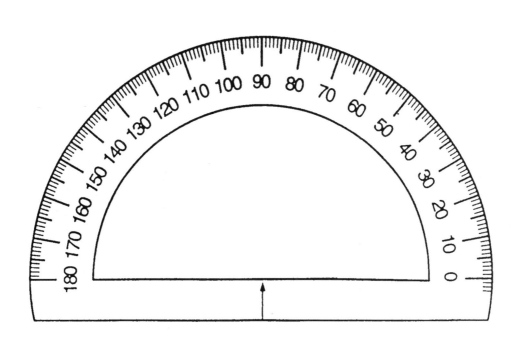

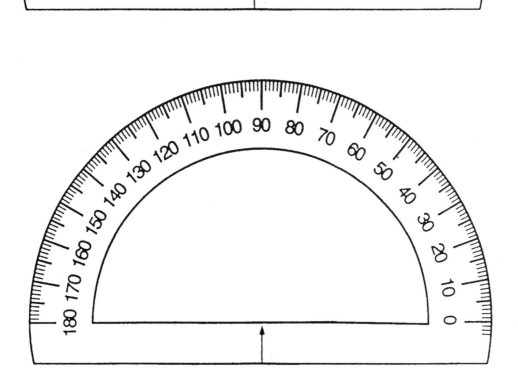

Place Value Graphics

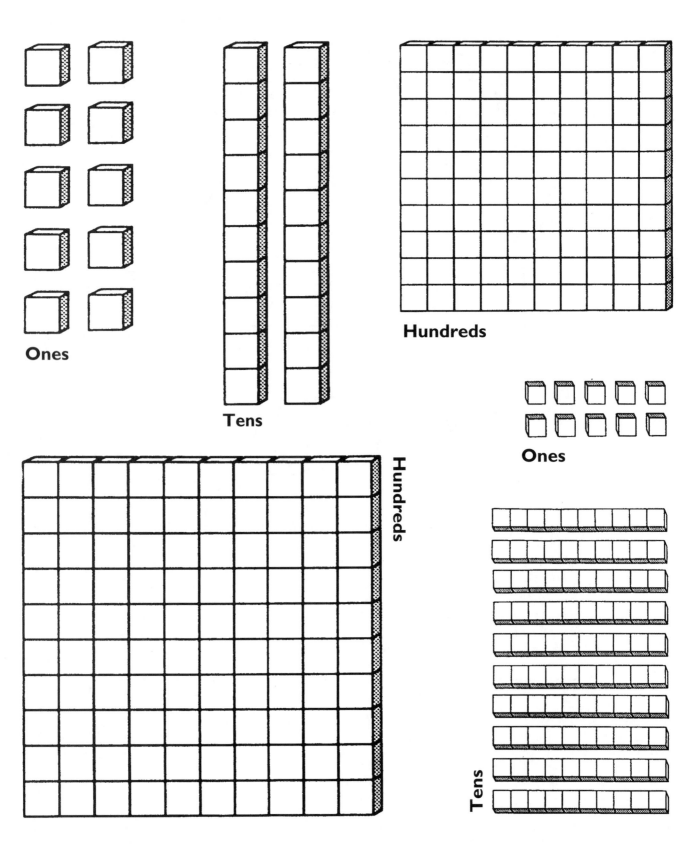

Ones

Tens

Hundreds

Ones

Hundreds

Tens

Small Number Array

1	2	3	4	5	6	7	8	9	10
11	12	13	14	15	16	17	18	19	20
21	22	23	24	25	26	27	28	29	30
31	32	33	34	35	36	37	38	39	40
41	42	43	44	45	46	47	48	49	50
51	52	53	54	55	56	57	58	59	60
61	62	63	64	65	66	67	68	69	70
71	72	73	74	75	76	77	78	79	80
81	82	83	84	85	86	87	88	89	90
91	92	93	94	95	96	97	98	99	100

Assignment:

Student Addition Table

+	0	1	2	3	4	5	6	7	8	9	10	11	12
0	0	1	2	3	4	5	6	7	8	9	10	11	12
1	1	2	3	4	5	6	7	8	9	10	11	12	13
2	2	3	4	5	6	7	8	9	10	11	12	13	14
3	3	4	5	6	7	8	9	10	11	12	13	14	15
4	4	5	6	7	8	9	10	11	12	13	14	15	16
5	5	6	7	8	9	10	11	12	13	14	15	16	17
6	6	7	8	9	10	11	12	13	14	15	16	17	18
7	7	8	9	10	11	12	13	14	15	16	17	18	19
8	8	9	10	11	12	13	14	15	16	17	18	19	20
9	9	10	11	12	13	14	15	16	17	18	19	20	21
10	10	11	12	13	14	15	16	17	18	19	20	21	22
11	11	12	13	14	15	16	17	18	19	20	21	22	23
12	12	13	14	15	16	17	18	19	20	21	22	23	24

Student Multiplication Table

×	0	1	2	3	4	5	6	7	8	9	10	11	12
0	0	0	0	0	0	0	0	0	0	0	0	0	0
1	0	1	2	3	4	5	6	7	8	9	10	11	12
2	0	2	4	6	8	10	12	14	16	18	20	22	24
3	0	3	6	9	12	15	18	21	24	27	30	33	36
4	0	4	8	12	16	20	24	28	32	36	40	44	48
5	0	5	10	15	20	25	30	35	40	45	50	55	60
6	0	6	12	18	24	30	36	42	48	54	60	66	72
7	0	7	14	21	28	35	42	49	56	63	70	77	84
8	0	8	16	24	32	40	48	56	64	72	80	88	96
9	0	9	18	27	36	45	54	63	72	81	90	99	108
10	0	10	20	30	40	50	60	70	80	90	100	110	120
11	0	11	22	33	44	55	66	77	88	99	110	121	132
12	0	12	24	36	48	60	72	84	96	108	120	132	144

Plotting Points

$(-, +)$ 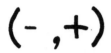 $(+, +)$

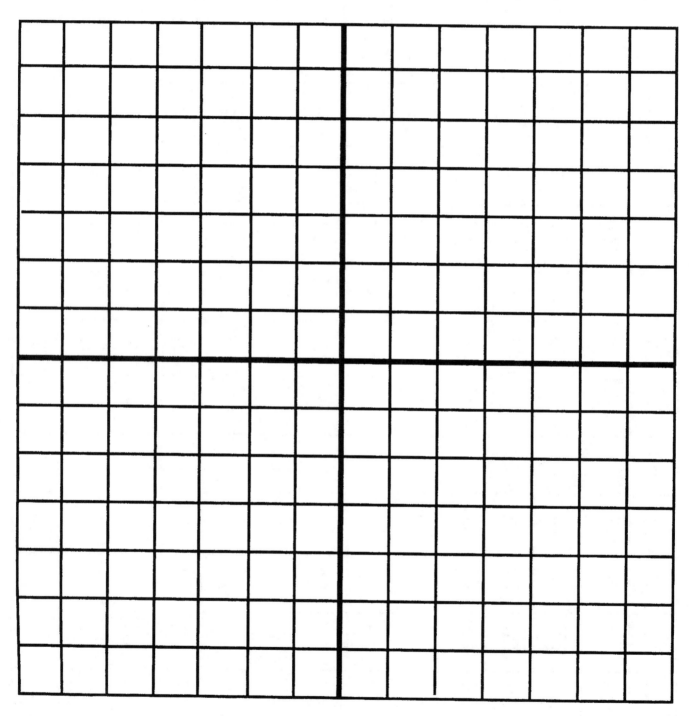

$(-, -)$ $(+, -)$

Addition Flashcards

$\begin{array}{r} 1 \\ +0 \\ \hline \end{array}$	$\begin{array}{r} 1 \\ +1 \\ \hline \end{array}$	$\begin{array}{r} 1 \\ +2 \\ \hline \end{array}$	$\begin{array}{r} 1 \\ +3 \\ \hline \end{array}$
$\begin{array}{r} 1 \\ +4 \\ \hline \end{array}$	$\begin{array}{r} 1 \\ +5 \\ \hline \end{array}$	$\begin{array}{r} 1 \\ +6 \\ \hline \end{array}$	$\begin{array}{r} 1 \\ +7 \\ \hline \end{array}$
$\begin{array}{r} 1 \\ +8 \\ \hline \end{array}$	$\begin{array}{r} 1 \\ +9 \\ \hline \end{array}$	$\begin{array}{r} 1 \\ +10 \\ \hline \end{array}$	$\begin{array}{r} 1 \\ +11 \\ \hline \end{array}$
$\begin{array}{r} 2 \\ +0 \\ \hline \end{array}$	$\begin{array}{r} 2 \\ +1 \\ \hline \end{array}$	$\begin{array}{r} 2 \\ +2 \\ \hline \end{array}$	$\begin{array}{r} 2 \\ +3 \\ \hline \end{array}$

Addition Flashcards

2 +4	2 +5	2 +6	2 +7
2 +8	2 +9	2 +10	2 +11
3 +0	3 +1	3 +2	3 +3
3 +4	3 +5	3 +6	3 +7

Addition Flashcards

3 +8	3 +9	3 +10	3 +11
4 +0	4 +1	4 +2	4 +3
4 +4	4 +5	4 +6	4 +7
4 +8	4 +9	4 +10	4 +11

Addition Flashcards

5 +0	5 +1	5 +2	5 +3
5 +4	5 +5	5 +6	5 +7
5 +8	5 +9	5 +10	5 +11
6 +0	6 +1	6 +2	6 +3

Addition Flashcards

6 +4	6 +5	6 +6	6 +7
6 +8	6 +9	6 +10	6 +11
7 +0	7 +1	7 +2	7 +3
7 +4	7 +5	7 +6	7 +7

Addition Flashcards

7 +8	7 +9	7 +10	7 +11
8 +0	8 +1	8 +2	8 +3
8 +4	8 +5	8 +6	8 +7
8 +8	8 +9	8 +10	8 +11

Addition Flashcards

$\begin{array}{r}9\\+0\\\hline\end{array}$	$\begin{array}{r}9\\+1\\\hline\end{array}$	$\begin{array}{r}9\\+2\\\hline\end{array}$	$\begin{array}{r}9\\+3\\\hline\end{array}$
$\begin{array}{r}9\\+4\\\hline\end{array}$	$\begin{array}{r}9\\+5\\\hline\end{array}$	$\begin{array}{r}9\\+6\\\hline\end{array}$	$\begin{array}{r}9\\+7\\\hline\end{array}$
$\begin{array}{r}9\\+8\\\hline\end{array}$	$\begin{array}{r}9\\+9\\\hline\end{array}$	$\begin{array}{r}9\\+10\\\hline\end{array}$	$\begin{array}{r}9\\+11\\\hline\end{array}$

Subtraction Flashcards

0 − 0	1 − 0	1 − 1	2 − 0
2 − 1	2 − 2	3 − 0	3 − 1
3 − 2	3 − 3	4 − 0	4 − 1
4 − 2	4 − 3	4 − 4	5 − 0

Subtraction Flashcards

5 -1	5 -2	5 -3	5 -4
5 -5	6 -0	6 -1	6 -2
6 -3	6 -4	6 -5	6 -6
7 -0	7 -1	7 -2	7 -3

Subtraction Flashcards

7 −4	7 −5	7 −6	7 −7
8 −0	8 −1	8 −2	8 −3
8 −4	8 −5	8 −6	8 −7
8 −8	9 −0	9 −1	9 −2

Subtraction Flashcards

9 -3	9 -4	9 -5	9 -6
9 -7	9 -8	9 -9	10 -0
10 -1	10 -2	10 -3	10 -4
10 -5	10 -6	10 -7	10 -8

Multiplication Flashcards

2 x4	2 x5	2 x6	2 x7
2 x8	2 x9	2 x10	2 x11
3 x0	3 x1	3 x2	3 x3
3 x4	3 x5	3 x6	3 x7

Multiplication Flashcards

3 x8	3 x9	3 x10	3 x11
4 x0	4 x1	4 x2	4 x3
4 x4	4 x5	4 x6	4 x7
4 x8	4 x9	4 x10	4 x11

Multiplication Flashcards

5 x0	5 x1	5 x2	5 x3
5 x4	5 x5	5 x6	5 x7
5 x8	5 x9	5 x10	5 x11
6 x0	6 x1	6 x2	6 x3

Multiplication Flashcards

6 x4	6 x5	6 x6	6 x7
6 x8	6 x9	6 x10	6 x11
7 x0	7 x1	7 x2	7 x3
7 x4	7 x5	7 x6	7 x7

Multiplication Flashcards

7 x8	7 x9	7 x10	7 x11
8 x0	8 x1	8 x2	8 x3
8 x4	8 x5	8 x6	8 x7
8 x8	8 x9	8 x10	8 x11

Multiplication Flashcards

9 x0	9 x1	9 x2	9 x3
9 x4	9 x5	9 x6	9 x7
9 x8	9 x9	9 x10	9 x11

Division Flashcards

$1 \div 1 =$	$3 \div 3 =$
	$3 \div 1 =$
	$2 \div 2 =$
	$2 \div 1 =$

Division Flashcards

$5 \div 5 =$	$6 \div 6 =$	$8 \div 2 =$	$9 \div 3 =$
$5 \div 1 =$	$6 \div 3 =$	$8 \div 1 =$	$9 \div 1 =$
$4 \div 2 =$	$6 \div 2 =$	$7 \div 7 =$	$8 \div 8 =$
$4 \div 1 =$	$6 \div 1 =$	$7 \div 1 =$	$8 \div 4 =$

Division Flashcards

$10 \div 5 =$	$12 \div 6 =$	$15 \div 3 =$	$16 \div 8 =$
$10 \div 2 =$	$12 \div 3 =$	$14 \div 7 =$	$16 \div 2 =$
$10 \div 1 =$	$12 \div 2 =$	$14 \div 2 =$	$16 \div 4 =$
$9 \div 9 =$	$10 \div 10 =$	$12 \div 4 =$	$15 \div 5 =$

Division Flashcards

$20 \div 2 =$	$21 \div 3 =$	$24 \div 4 =$	$27 \div 3 =$
$18 \div 6 =$	$20 \div 10 =$	$24 \div 3 =$	$25 \div 5 =$
$18 \div 9 =$	$20 \div 5 =$	$24 \div 2 =$	$24 \div 8 =$
$18 \div 2 =$	$20 \div 4 =$	$21 \div 7 =$	$24 \div 6 =$

Division Flashcards

$30 \div 5 =$	$35 \div 5 =$	$42 \div 7 =$	$48 \div 8 =$
$28 \div 7 =$	$35 \div 7 =$	$40 \div 8 =$	$48 \div 6 =$
$28 \div 4 =$	$32 \div 8 =$	$40 \div 5 =$	$49 \div 7 =$
$27 \div 9 =$	$32 \div 4 =$	$36 \div 6 =$	$42 \div 6 =$

Division Flashcards

$56 \div 7 =$	$54 \div 6 =$	$54 \div 9 =$	$50 \div 5 =$
$64 \div 8 =$	$63 \div 7 =$	$63 \div 9 =$	$56 \div 8 =$
			$72 \div 9 =$

Dinah Zike Academy   www.dzacademy.com

Dinah Zike is proud to introduce the Dinah Zike Academy, a teacher training institute outside of San Antonio in the beautiful and historic Texas Hill Country.

Dinah: *It has always been my dream to have a location for teachers to immerse themselves in a fully developed, hands-on lab setting that will provide strategies to address diverse learners, meet state and national benchmarks, and build student learning skills for life. I also want to provide the opportunity for teachers to become Dinah Zike Certified trainers for their district, state, or nationwide, because I can't physically reach all the teachers who want to learn more about Foldables®, VKVs,® and my other teaching strategies.*

In three-day, jam-packed sessions at the Academy, Dinah and/or DZA's pro facilitators will engage and immerse you in the power and potential of 3-D interactive graphic organizers, dynamic and efficient classroom organization, and effective teaching strategies across age-grade levels and content areas. Research grounding, implementation for a variety of learners, and practicality are built in. A session maximum of 24 participants allows for hands-on individual and small-group work, technology use, and direct application to participants' teaching practices. Some seminars are cross-curricular and targeted to either elementary or secondary levels. Others are focused on specific content/subject areas, such as science, mathematics, social studies, and reading/language arts.

The expansive Academy is well-equipped with group and individual classrooms, high-speed Internet access, computer work stations, working design areas and tools, easily replicable supply stations, displays and publishing centers plus resources including artifacts, a research and reference library, and the list goes on.

The Academy is located in the heart of the historic and charming village of Comfort, Texas, in the beautiful Texas Hill country, 45 minutes from San Antonio and 1½ hours from Austin. Most convenient airport is San Antonio. Antiquing, shopping, golfing, fishing, bicycling, sightseeing, caving, natural and historic-site adventuring are popular area pursuits. Or just relaxing on the porch of your B&B!

Testimonial: "*I just returned from the Dinah Zike Academy, and I'm overwhelmed with the vast amount of information provided. This is my 37th year in education, and I've never enjoyed a course of study as much as the Academy.*"

For More Information, or to reserve your spot:

WEBSITE: www.dzacademy.com
PHONE: 830-995-3800
FAX: 830-995-3713
EMAIL: dzi@hctc.net
DZ Academy, P. O. Box 340, Comfort TX 78013

Other Elementary Books by Dinah Zike   www.dinah.com   1-800-99DINAH

Big Book Series for Elementary

Foldables® for Every Subject

You've attended a Dinah Zike workshop at your school or at a teacher's conference and are ready to get started using 3-D graphic organizers in the classroom, but you need help generating all of those great ideas. Now Dinah has combined instructions for her most popular folds, full-co... ... ...hed examples, and lists of thousands of ideas she has collected over her thirty+ years ... using graphic organizers. The lists of ideas are divided by the skill being taug... skill or concept, and how many Foldable parts are needed so you can quickly ... ic organizer. Books are subject specific and geared towards elementary level or middle school/high school level.

Elementary Big Book Series

Big Book of Social Studies (K-6) CCC103..$19.95
Big Book of Texas History (K-7) CCC105..$19.95
Big Book of United States History (5-12) CCC107..$19.95
Big Book of World History (6-12) CCC108..$19.95
Big Book of Math (K-6) CCC106..$19.95
Big Book of Science (K-6) CCC111..$19.95

More Books by Dinah Zike   To see all of Dinah's books and materials visit www.dinah.com or call 1-800-99DINAH for a free catalog.

This 148-page book is the sequel to Dinah's *Big Book of Books and Activities*. It expands the use of manipulatives presented in *Big Book of Books and Activities*, and it introduces 14 folds not found in that book. The back section contains 64 duplicable pages of Dinah's publishing center graphics.
CCC91..$19.95

The award-winning *Big Book of Books and Activities* contains nearly all of Dinah's Foldables and presents hundreds of examples of what you can teach with them. Since its 1989 debut, it has become an education classic, and it is used internationally by experienced teachers, student teachers, and home schooling parents alike. *CCC100..$19.95*

For years, teachers have encouraged Dinah to organize her manipulative holiday ideas into a book. Now it's here. The *Big Book of Holiday Activities* contains 180 pages of monthly holiday manipulatives and activities and art patterns for the K-5 student. The book also contains lists of story starters, historic dates, and important birthdays to be used as holiday research and writing projects.
CCC83..$24.95

Dinah's K-6 national bestseller is back, updated, and full color! A comprehensive teacher's guide to help you creatively manage your time, your energy, and the materials in your classroom. *Classroom Organization, It Can Be Done, K-6 Revised Edition* is filled with practical and effective ideas to make your life easier and your teaching more effective!
CCC99..$24.95

Join Dinah's free *E-group* at www.dinah.com or include your e-mail address on your order form. The *E-group* is an easy way for Dinah to keep in touch with teachers while announcing new books and sharing teaching ideas. Privacy is important to us; therefore, we will not sell, rent, or give your name or address to anyone.

Equivalency Flips™

Dinah's Newest Math Manipulative
One sheet of colored 8½ x 11 paper magically folds to teach multiple equivalencies! For example, the "**Cup and Ounces Equivalency Flip**" (left) folds to form a tabbed activity that illustrates the relationship between cups, ounces, tablespoons, and milliliters. Others illustrate fractions, percentages, time (right), measurement, weight, and more. Quickly and easily make a classroom set: just pop out the diecut sections, fold, and glue. **Each packet contains a classroom set of 12 identical diecut color sheets with full-color instructions, or get a mixed set with one of each.**

New Product Line!

EACH PACKET CONTAINS
12 IDENTICAL SHEETS

EF1 **Mixed Set:** One of each, 16 sheets total
EF2 **1/2, 1/4, 1/8** (+decimals & percentages)
EF3 **1/3, 1/6, 1/12** (+parts of a dozen)
EF4 **Percentages** (+fractions and decimals)
EF5 **Decimals** (+percentages, fractions)
EF6 **Hour** halves, quarters, minutes, seconds
EF7 **Money** dollar, half-dollars, quarters, dimes
EF8 **Gallon,** quarts, pints, ounces, (+ml)
EF9 **Cup and Ounces** (+tablespoons, milliliters)
EF10 **Liter** (+quarts, pints, ounces)
EF11 **Mile** (+meters)
EF12 **Kilometer** (+feet)
EF13 **Meter** (+inches, feet, yard)
EF14 **Yard** (+centimeters)
EF15 **Music** Whole, half, quarter, eighth notes
EF16 **Year** (+seasons, days, solstices, equinoxes)
EF17 **Pounds, Ounces, Grams**
EF18 **Custom Mixed Packet:** Two titles, 6+6, your choice
EF2 thru EF17...$14.00
EF1 & EF18...$18.00

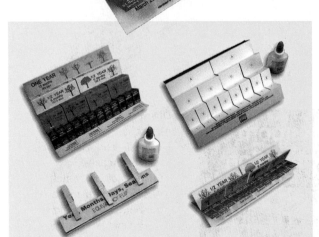

EASY TO MAKE Quickly and easily make a classroom set. Pop out the diecut strips, fold the sheet like an accordion, and glue the back to make a three- dimensional **Equivalency Flip.**

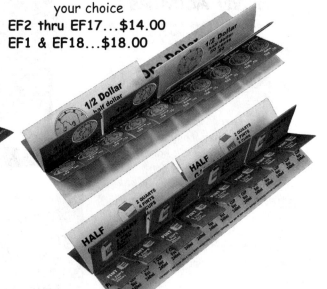

Line Art Library CD   Over 1000 illustrations!

Introduction

We commissioned an illustrator who loves working with kids, Becky Hall, to draw **over 1000** different illustrations appropriate for language development activities with PreK to 2nd grade students. The art on this CD fits perfectly on Foldables and VKVs, or it can be enlarged and used on posters and charts. Many of you purchased this book with the CD. Those of you who did not can purchase the CD separately if you think in hindsight that it will be helpful.

CD-101........................ $20.00

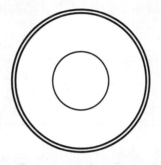

Line Art Library
Over 1200 duplicable illustrations
PreK - 2 Phonics, Spelling, & Vocabulary

Perfect for use with Dinah Zike's
Phonics & Spelling Foldables®
and VKV™ Flashcards.

Artwork by Becky Hall
© Dinah-Might Adventures LP

Organization

Line Art Library CD is organized in easy to use folders:
- Antonyms
- Blends
- Compound Words
- Consonants
- CVC
- CVCE
- CVVC
- Digraphs
- Diphthongs
- Heteronyms
- Homophones
- Homographs
- Phonograms
- Prefixes
- Suffixes
- Syllables

The line art on this CD can be printed, colored, and glued onto flashcards, posters, charts, and bulletin boards.

Dual-Cut Scissors

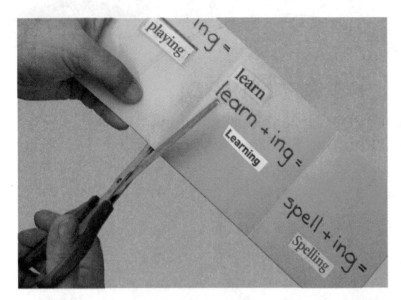

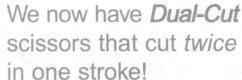

We now have *Dual-Cut* scissors that cut *twice* in one stroke!

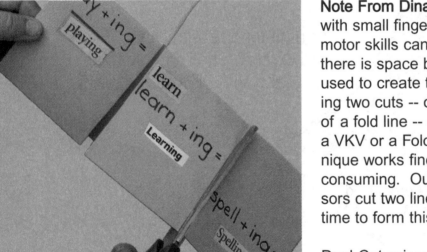

Note From Dinah: Young children with small fingers and poor fine-motor skills can lift tabs easier if there is space between them. I used to create this space by making two cuts -- one on each side of a fold line -- every time I•made a VKV or a Foldable. This technique works fine, but it is time consuming. Our Dual-Cut scissors cut two lines at the same time to form this wide space.

Dual-Cut scissors are great for making the flaps and moveable tabs on your Foldables and VKVs. They work exceptionally well with index weight paper and poster board.

CCC95............................ $14.00

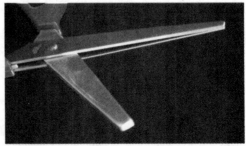